grade 2

ELD
Practice Book

PEARSON

Glenview, Illinois • Boston, Massachusetts • Chandler, Arizona • Upper Saddle River, New Jersey

ISBN-13: 978-0-328-63482-8
ISBN-10:   0-328-63482-4

6 7 8 9   V0N4 13

Unit 1 Exploration

Unit 2 Working Together

Unit 3 Creative Ideas

Name _____

Exploring Communities

Vocabulary

city	friends	community	different
country	busy	crops	

Directions Finish these sentences. Use words from the box.

1. My two best _____ live next door.

2. A _____ has many cars.

3. There are farm animals in the _____.

4. Farmers grow _____ to sell.

5. People have _____ jobs.

6. People at an office are _____ working.

7. My _____ is a nice place to live.

_____

Directions Use one word from above in a sentence of your own. Use the sentence starter if you need help.

I live in...

8. _____

_____

Name _____

Short Vowels

Directions Fill in the vowel to finish each word.

a e i o u

1.  m __ p

2.  p __ n

3.  b __ t

4.  s __ nk

5.  d __ ck

---

Directions Finish the sentences. Use the words you wrote above.

6. I write with a _____.

7. I wash in the _____.

8. I use a _____ to clean the floor.

9. I hit the ball with the _____.

10. I saw a _____ swimming on the pond.

Describing

Directions Circle the words that tell about the people in the sentences.

1. John looks sleepy.

2. Ella is tall.

3. José feels lonely.

4. Kate is silly.

5. Maria seems happy.

Character and Setting

Directions Write about your classroom. Use words that tell about that place.

_____

_____

_____

_____

_____

_____

Name _____

Complete Sentences

Directions Draw a line under each complete sentence.

1. I like my community.

2. The crops

3. In another city

4. I help my friends.

5. There are many cars in the street.

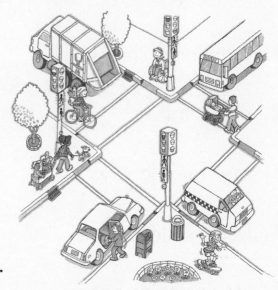

Directions Finish the sentence frames to make complete sentences about your community.

6. There are _____ in my community.

7. Everyone is _____ in my community.

Name _____

Produce Language

My Weekly Concept Journal

Directions Write your answers in the space provided.

Day 1 _____

_____

_____

_____

_____

Day 2 _____

_____

_____

_____

_____

_____

Day 3 _____

_____

_____

_____

_____

Day 4 _____

_____

_____

_____

_____

Name _____

Produce Language

My Weekly Concept Journal

Directions Write 2 or 3 sentences to answer the weekly question.

What can we learn by exploring different communities?

_____

_____

_____

_____

_____

_____

_____

_____

_____

_____

_____

_____

_____

_____

_____

_____

_____

_____

Name _____

Exploring Space

Vocabulary

astronauts	space	world
shuttle	work	

Directions Finish these sentences. Use words from the box.

1. The space _____ travels to and from Earth.

2. My parents _____ in the same office.

3. A rocket can take people up into _____.

4. Exploring space can teach us about our _____.

5. _____ walked on the moon.

_____

Directions Use two words from above in sentences of your own. Use these sentence starters if you need help.
Stars are...   Sally Ride...

6. _____

7. _____

Name _____

Long Vowels

Directions Fill in the vowel to finish each word.

a   o   u

1.    c ___ ge

2.   c ___ be

3.    h ___ se

---

Directions Finish the sentences. Use the new words you created above.

4. The bird was in a _____.

5. I use a _____ to water the flowers.

6. I took an ice _____ from the freezer.

Summarizing

Directions Circle the sentences that summarize.

1. The main idea is that people should tell the truth.

2. Her name is Sally Ride.

3. The story is about an explorer.

4. The poem is about a tree.

5. The book is at home.

Main Idea and Details

Directions Read the sentences about astronauts. Draw a line under the sentence that tells the main idea. Draw circles around the sentences that tell details.

6. Astronauts float in space.

7. Sally Ride used a robot arm.

8. Astronauts have fun at work.

Name _____

Subjects

Directions Read each sentence. Circle the subjects.

1. That dog barks all the time.

2. The cup is broken.

3. Carlos plays soccer.

4. The leaves changed color.

5. Vita has a new bike.

_____

Directions Write sentences about exploring space.
Underline the subjects.

_____

_____

_____

_____

Produce Language

My Weekly Concept Journal

Directions Write your answers in the space provided.

Day 1 _____

_____

_____

_____

Day 2 _____

_____

_____

_____

_____

Day 3 _____

_____

_____

_____

Day 4 _____

_____

_____

_____

Name _____

Produce Language

My Weekly Concept Journal

Directions Write 2 or 3 sentences to answer the weekly question.

What can we learn by exploring space?

_____

_____

_____

_____

_____

_____

_____

_____

_____

_____

_____

_____

_____

_____

_____

_____

_____

_____

_____

Exploring Nature

Vocabulary

bear	mother	straight
climb	far away	take care

Directions Finish these sentences. Use words from the box.

1. I like to go places with my _____ .

2. We drive to places that are _____ from home.

3. I help _____ of our class pets.

4. I saw a _____ in the woods.

5. My baby brother can _____ out of his crib.

6. I use a ruler to draw a _____ line.

_____

Directions Use two words from above in sentences of your own. Use these sentence starters if you need help.

A baby needs...   Some animals...

7. _____

   _____

8. _____

   _____

Name _____

Consonant Blends

Directions Write the word that names each picture.
Use the words in the box.

crib	straw	sled	lamp	desk

1.  _____

2.  _____

3. _____

4. _____

5. _____

Directions Finish the sentences. Use the words you wrote above.

6. I drank my milk with a _____.

7. The baby sleeps in a _____.

8. I work at my _____.

9. Please turn off the _____.

10. I ride my _____ when it snows.

Name _____

Literary Analysis

Directions Finish these sentences. Use words from the box.

Rosa	jumped	like	teacher

1. Our _____ was sick today.

2. _____ is my best friend.

3. I _____ animals.

4. Paco _____ into the puddle.

Character, Setting, and Plot

Directions Think of a story you know well. Fill in the chart below. Write about the characters, setting, and plot of the story.

Characters	Plot	Setting
	First: Next: Last:	

Name _____

Predicate

Directions Read the sentences. Circle the predicates.

1. Plants need water.

2. Miguel saw the deer.

3. Our class went on a field trip.

4. Bears like to eat berries.

5. Animals take care of each other.

Directions Finish the sentences below.

6. Pam and I _____ .

7. The car _____ .

8. An animal _____ .

Produce Language

My Weekly Concept Journal

Directions Write your answers in the space provided.

Day 1 _____

_____

_____

_____

_____

Day 2 _____

_____

_____

_____

_____

Day 3 _____

_____

_____

_____

_____

Day 4 _____

_____

_____

_____

_____

Name _____

Produce Language

My Weekly Concept Journal

Directions Write 2 or 3 sentences to answer the weekly question.

What can we discover by exploring nature?

_____

_____

_____

_____

_____

_____

_____

_____

_____

_____

_____

_____

_____

_____

_____

_____

_____

_____

_____

Before We Explore

Vocabulary

first aid kit	water	warm
hiking	planning	

Directions Finish these sentences. Use words from the box.

1. Jack went _____ in the woods.

2. It was a _____ day.

3. He drank a lot of _____ .

4. He brought a _____ in case he got a cut.

5. He is _____ to do this again soon.

Directions Use two words from above in sentences of your own. Use these sentence starters if you need help.
You should take...   It is fun to...

6. _____

_____

7. _____

_____

Name _____

The Endings -s, -ed, -ing

Directions Add the endings to each word to make a new word.

1.   think + ing _____

2.   skip + ed _____

3.   bake + ed _____

4.   smile + s _____

5.   sit + ing _____

Directions Finish the sentences. Use the words you wrote above.

6. Dad _____ a pie.

7. She _____ all the time.

8. Lao and I _____ all the way home.

9. I was _____ about the test.

10. They are _____ on the bench.

Explaining

Directions Tell why you do these things.

1. I brush my teeth to _____ .

2. I wear a hat to _____ .

3. I take an umbrella to _____ .

4. I go to the library to _____ .

Main Idea and Details

Directions Read the sentences. Circle the main idea.

5. It is important to dress warmly during winter.

Mittens keep your hands warm.

Boots keep your feet warm and dry.

6. Luis plays soccer.

He also plays basketball.

Luis is good at most sports.

Name _____

Statements and Questions

Directions Add the correct end punctuation to each sentence.

1. What is your favorite color _____

2. How are you getting home _____

3. I am planning a trip _____

4. I packed water and a first aid kit _____

5. Do you want to come with me _____

Directions Write a statement and a question. Be sure to use the correct end punctuation for each sentence.

_____

_____

_____

_____

_____

Produce Language

My Weekly Concept Journal

Directions Write your answers in the space provided.

Day 1 _____

_____

_____

_____

Day 2 _____

_____

_____

_____

_____

Day 3 _____

_____

_____

_____

_____

Day 4 _____

_____

_____

_____

Name _____

Produce Language

My Weekly Concept Journal

Directions Write 2 or 3 sentences to answer the weekly question.

How can we prepare for exploration?

_____

_____

_____

_____

_____

_____

_____

_____

_____

_____

_____

_____

_____

_____

_____

_____

_____

_____

_____

Exploration's Answers

Vocabulary

birds	**monkey**	**much**
butterflies	**learn**	**teach**

Directions Finish these sentences. Use words from the box.

1. How _____ do you know about animals?

2. _____ lay eggs in a nest.

3. _____ seem to float in the air.

4. A _____ swings from tree to tree.

5. There is a lot to _____ about animals.

6. Exploring can _____ us about nature.

Directions Use two words from above in sentences of your own. Use these sentence starters if you need help.
School is where...   Rain forests are...

7. _____

_____

8. _____

_____

Name _____

Consonant Digraphs

Directions Fill in the digraphs to finish each word.

wh   **ch**   **tch**   **sh**   **th**

1. ___ ___ a l e

2. ___ ___ i l d

3. m a ___ ___ ___

4. f i ___ ___

5. b a ___ ___

Directions Finish the sentences. Use the words you wrote above.

6. There are bubbles in the _____.

7. The _____ was sick.

8. Dad lit the fire with a _____.

9. A _____ is a very large animal.

10. I take care of my pet _____.

30 Exploration's Answers • Unit 1, Week 5

Defining

Directions Finish the sentences. Use the words below.

butterfly

parrot

banana

baby

1. A _____ is a bird.

2. A _____ is an insect.

3. A _____ is a person.

4. A _____ is a fruit.

Classify and Categorize

Directions Put the words below in groups.

cat   tree   flower   monkey   grass   dog

Plants	Animals

Name _____

Commands and Exclamations

Directions Add the correct end punctuation to each sentence.

1. I love fruit _____

2. Please close the door _____

3. You're the best _____

4. That's great _____

5. Go home _____

Directions Write a command and an exclamation. Be sure to use the correct end punctuation for each sentence.

_____

_____

_____

_____

_____

Produce Language

My Weekly Concept Journal

Directions Write your answers in the space provided.

Day 1 _____

_____

_____

_____

Day 2 _____

_____

_____

_____

Day 3 _____

_____

_____

_____

Day 4 _____

_____

_____

_____

Name _____

Produce Language

My Weekly Concept Journal

Directions Write 2 or 3 sentences to answer the weekly question.

How does exploration help us find answers?

_____

_____

_____

_____

_____

_____

_____

_____

_____

_____

_____

_____

_____

_____

_____

_____

_____

_____

Exploring Communities

Directions Write the letter of the phrase that gives the meaning of each word.

1. ____ city   **A.** land outside of town

2. ____ country   **B.** full of many people or things

3. ____ friends   **C.** all the people living in one place

4. ____ busy   **D.** a very large town

5. ____ community   **E.** not the same

6. ____ crops   **F.** plants that a farmer grows

7. ____ different   **G.** people who you like very much

Short Vowels

The vowels are **a, e, i, o,** and **u.**

Directions Fill in the vowel to finish each word.

8.

c ___ n

9.

p ___ n

10.

c ___ p

Name _____

Describing/Character and Setting

Describing words tell about the characters and setting of a story.

Directions Describe a character in a story you like.

1. Character: _____

_____

Complete Sentences

A **complete sentence** tells a complete thought. It ends with punctuation.

Directions Finish the sentence frames to make complete sentences.

2. The book I like best is _____

3. I like school because _____

Think, Talk, and Write

Directions Reread **Exploring Communities** and **Communities** on Student Worktext pages 22–23.

4. Talk about exploring communities with a partner. Read your Weekly Concept Journal on page 10. Change or add to what you wrote.

Exploring Space

Directions Write the letter of the phrase that gives the meaning of each word.

1. _____ astronauts

    A. Earth and all the people and things in it

2. _____ shuttle

    B. the area away from Earth, where the sun and stars are

3. _____ space

    C. to do a job

4. _____ world

    D. a vehicle that can fly into space and return to Earth

5. _____ work

    E. people who travel into space

Long Vowels

The long vowel sound is the same as the letter's name.

Directions Fill in the vowel to finish the words.

6.

   c _____ ne

7.

   r _____ be

8.

   fl _____ te

Name _____

Summarizing/Main Idea and Details

The **main idea** is the most important idea in a story. The **details** tell us more about the main idea. A **summary** tells the main idea.

Directions Draw a line under the sentence that tells the main idea. Draw a circle around the sentence that tells a detail.

1. We do not know if there is another planet like Earth.

2. There is a lot we do not know about space.

Subjects

Subjects are the people, places, or things that sentences are about.

Directions Circle the subjects.

3. Sally Ride was the first American woman in space.

4. Stars can only be seen at night.

5. I want to study space.

Think, Talk, and Write

Directions Reread **Exploring Space** and **Sally Ride** on Student Worktext pages 28–29.

6. Talk about exploring space with a partner. Read your Weekly Concept Journal on page 16. Change or add to what you wrote.

Exploring Nature

Directions Write the letter of the phrase that gives the meaning of each word.

1. _____ bear

A. a female parent

2. _____ climb

B. to give another person or animal things they need

3. _____ mother

C. to go up something

4. _____ far away

D. not bending or curved

5. _____ straight

E. a large, wild animal with thick fur

6. _____ take care

F. not close by

Consonant Blends

Two or three consonants can blend together to make a sound.

Directions Write the consonant blend that finishes each word.

   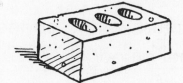   

7. _____ ing   **8.** _____ ick   **9.** ma _____

Name _____

Literary Analysis/Character, Setting, and Plot

In English, we usually first tell *who* or *what* the sentence is about. Then, we say what the person or thing is or does.

Directions Finish these sentences. Use these words:
Clara, jumped, brother

1. _____ is going to school.

2. My _____ likes to eat apples.

3. Pam _____ over the fence.

Predicate

The **predicate** tells something about the subject of the sentence.

Directions Finish the sentences below.

4. The cat _____.

5. Maya _____.

Think, Talk, and Write

Directions Reread **Exploring Nature** and **The Bears** on Student Worktext pages 34–35.

6. Talk about exploring nature with a partner. Read your Weekly Concept Journal on page 22. Change or add to what you wrote.

Name _____

Before We Explore

Directions Write the letter of the phrase that gives the meaning of each word.

1. _____ first aid kit

A. the clear liquid in rain, rivers, and lakes

2. _____ hiking

B. thinking about how to do something

3. _____ water

C. taking a long walk in the country or in the mountains

4. _____ planning

D. slightly hot, but not too hot

5. _____ warm

E. a box that holds medicine and bandages to help someone who is sick or hurt

The Endings -s, -ed, -ing

Endings can change the meaning of a word. The endings *-s, -ed,* and *-ing* change the meaning of a verb.

Directions Add the endings to each base word to make a new word. Then use the new word in a sentence.

6. stop + ed _____

Sentence: _____

7. hike + s _____

Sentence: _____

Name _____

Explaining/Main Idea and Details

Words and sentences tell about people and things. They also tell why a person does something.

Directions Read the sentences. Circle the words that tell what Sam did. Draw a line under the words that tell us why.

1. Sam washed his hands to get the paint off.

2. Sam drank water because he was thirsty.

Statements and Questions

Statements are sentences that tell us something. **Questions** are sentences that ask something.

Directions Write a question and a statement. Include the correct end punctuation.

3. Question: _____

4. Statement: _____

Think, Talk, and Write

Directions Reread **Before We Explore** and **Getting Ready** on Student Worktext pages 40–41.

5. Talk with a partner about ways to prepare for exploring. Read your Weekly Concept Journal on page 28. Change or add to what you wrote.

Exploration's Answers

Directions Write the letter of the phrase that gives the meaning of each word.

1. _____ birds

A. a small furry animal that has a long tail and climbs trees

2. _____ butterflies

B. animals with wings and feathers that lay eggs and usually can fly

3. _____ monkey

C. to give lessons about any subject

4. _____ learn

D. insects that have large wings with bright colors

5. _____ teach

E. to get information or facts about something

Consonant Digraphs

A **digraph** is a pair of letters that makes one sound when combined.

Directions Write each word. Circle the digraph.

6. _____

7. _____

8. _____

Name _____

Defining/Classify and Categorize

Grouping tells about kinds of things. We **classify,** or **categorize,** when we put like things into groups.

Directions Name three things you might find in each group.

Colors	Sports	People

Commands and Exclamations

Commands tell someone to do something. **Exclamations** show strong emotion, such as surprise or excitement.

Directions Write a command and an exclamation. Be sure to use the correct end punctuation for each sentence.

1. Command: _____

2. Exclamation: _____

Think, Talk, and Write

Directions Reread **Exploration's Answers** and **Rain Forest Animals** on Student Worktext pages 46–47.

3. Talk with a partner about learning from exploring. Read your Weekly Concept Journal on page 34. Change or add to what you wrote.

Name _____

Helping People in Danger

Vocabulary

family	dangerous
firefighter	listen

Directions Finish the sentences. Use words from the box.

1. She has a big _____ .

2. A house fire is very _____ .

3. A _____ knows how to put out a fire.

4. It is important to _____ to grown-ups.

Directions Use three words from above in sentences of your own. Use these sentence starters if you need help.

People like to...   In an emergency...
A fire plan can...

5. _____

_____

6. _____

_____

7. _____

_____

Name _____

The /är/ and /ôr/ Sounds

Directions Write the word that names the picture.
Use these words: **store, fork, car, barn.**

1.  _____

2. _____

3.  _____

4. _____

Directions Finish the sentences. Use the words you wrote above.

5. The cows are in the _____ .

6. Anna put a _____ next to each plate.

7. Mom bought milk at the _____ .

8. The _____ had a flat tire.

Sequencing

Directions Read the sentences. Circle the words that tell order.

1. The fire alarm went off last.

2. First, the smoke came out the window.

3. Next, we saw flames.

4. Everyone got out first.

5. The firefighter climbed a ladder next.

Sequence

Directions Write the order of the sentences. Use **1, 2,** and **3.**

Next, I swung the bat. ___
Last, I hit a home run. ___
First, the pitcher threw the ball. ___

Name _____

Nouns

Directions Circle the nouns. Write whether the noun names a **person, place,** or **thing.**

1. The fire was small. _____

2. The boy called 9-1-1. _____

3. A firefighter came to help. _____

4. The house did not burn down. _____

_____

Directions Choose a noun from the box to finish each sentence.

hose	alarm	truck
smoke	fire	

5. We heard the _____ .

6. There was a _____ !

7. _____ came out the windows.

8. Firefighters arrived in a red _____ .

9. They put the fire out with water from their _____ .

Produce Language

My Weekly Concept Journal

Directions Write your answers in the space provided.

Day 1 _____

_____

_____

_____

_____

Day 2 _____

_____

_____

_____

_____

Day 3 _____

_____

_____

_____

_____

Day 4 _____

_____

_____

_____

_____

Name _____

Produce Language

My Weekly Concept Journal

Directions Write 2 or 3 sentences to answer the weekly question.

How can we help each other in dangerous situations?

_____

_____

_____

_____

_____

_____

_____

_____

_____

_____

_____

_____

_____

_____

_____

_____

Name _____

Changing History

Vocabulary

hurricane	damage	worst
rebuild	great	couldn't

Directions Finish the sentences. Use words from the box.

1. It was the _____ storm in years.

2. The _____ destroyed the city.

3. There was a lot of _____ .

4. Many houses _____ be saved.

5. People worked together to _____ .

6. They made a _____ difference.

Directions Use two words from above in sentences of your own. Use these sentence starters if you need help.
A bad storm...   Hurricane Katrina...

7. _____

8. _____

Name _____

Contractions

Directions Write the words as contractions.

1. can not _____

2. we will _____

3. I am _____

4. he is _____

5. they will _____

Directions Finish these sentences. Use the contractions you wrote above.

6. _____ sitting next to me.

7. _____ cooking breakfast myself.

8. My little brother _____ tie his shoe.

9. _____ watch our cat while we are away.

10. _____ be home next week.

Describing

Directions Circle the verb in each sentence.

1. Marta is a good helper.

2. We are best friends.

3. Berto is smiling.

4. I am sleepy.

5. They are winning.

Author's Purpose

Directions Read the sentences below. Underline the describing words. Circle the verbs *am*, *is*, and *are*.

I am scared. A hurricane is coming. We have to leave our house. My parents are scared, too. We are all worried.

6. What does the author feel?

_____

Name _____

Proper Nouns

Directions Circle the proper nouns.

1. I live in San Francisco.

2. Daniel fixed the toy.

3. We drove across the Golden Gate Bridge.

4. My best friend lives on Oak Street.

5. Grandma Dora lives in Mexico.

Directions Finish the sentences. Use a proper noun.

6. My name is _____.

7. I live on _____.

8. I want to travel to _____ someday.

Name _____

Produce Language

My Weekly Concept Journal

Directions Write your answers in the space provided.

Day 1 _____
_____
_____
_____
_____

Day 2 _____
_____
_____
_____
_____

Day 3 _____
_____
_____
_____
_____

Day 4 _____
_____
_____
_____
_____

Name _____

Produce Language

My Weekly Concept Journal

Directions Write 2 or 3 sentences to answer the weekly question.

How has working together changed history?

_____

_____

_____

_____

_____

_____

_____

_____

_____

_____

_____

_____

_____

_____

_____

_____

_____

_____

Meeting Needs

Vocabulary

tools	whole	community
enough	work	

Directions Finish the sentences. Use words from the box.

1. We _____ together to make our garden nice.

2. It is not _____ just to plant some seeds.

3. Weeds can take over the _____ garden.

4. You will need _____ to get the job done.

5. We made a _____ garden.

Directions Use two words from above in sentences of your own. Use these sentence starters if you need help.
I want to...   A garden...

6. _____

_____

7. _____

_____

Name _____

The /ėr/ Sound

Directions Finish the words. Use **er, ir,** or **ur.**

1. t ___ tle

2. g ___ l

3. sh ___ t

4. p ___ ch

5. t ___ key

Directions Finish the sentences. Use the words you wrote above.

6. Anita is the tallest _____ in our class.

7. The bird sat on a _____ .

8. The _____ has a hard shell.

9. Carmen has a _____ on her farm.

10. I wore the red _____ .

Asking Questions

Directions Circle the question words in the sentences below.

1. Who is picking you up today?

2. Where is the pencil?

3. What is for dinner?

4. Where are we going?

5. Who wants to go first?

Author's Purpose

Directions Read the paragraph below. What question is the author answering?

Plants need water. They need air. Plants also need room to grow. Most of all, plants need sunlight.

6. _____

Name _____

Singular and Plural Nouns

Directions Read the sentences. Circle the singular nouns. Underline the plural nouns.

1. Seeds grow into plants.

2. The girls and boys are working together.

3. The carrots are ready to pick.

4. Please do not pick that flower.

5. There are two trees in front
of the school.

Directions Finish these sentences. Use words from the box.

players	player

6. My brother is a baseball _____.

7. All of the _____ had fun.

Produce Language

My Weekly Concept Journal

Directions Write your answers in the space provided.

Day 1 _____

_____

_____

_____

_____

Day 2 _____

_____

_____

_____

_____

Day 3 _____

_____

_____

_____

_____

Day 4 _____

_____

_____

_____

_____

Name _____

Produce Language

My Weekly Concept Journal

Directions Write 2 or 3 sentences to answer the weekly question.

How can we work together to meet people's needs?

_____

_____

_____

_____

_____

_____

_____

_____

_____

_____

_____

_____

_____

_____

_____

_____

_____

Working Together

Vocabulary

band	people	probably
instruments	imagine	

Directions Finish the sentences. Use the words in the box.

1. Many _____ like music.

2. Some play in a _____ .

3. You have _____ heard one before.

4. I can't _____ a parade without one.

5. Different _____ sound nice together.

Directions Use two words from above in sentences of your own. Use these sentence starters if you need help.
A parade has...   **Working together...**

6. _____

_____

7. _____

_____

Name _____

Adding -s, -es, -ies

Directions Write the plural form of each word.

1. key _____

2. match _____

3.  bench _____

4.  puppy _____

Directions Finish the sentences. Use the words you wrote above.

5. We sat on _____ at the park.

6. We put _____ in the salad.

7. The _____ were so cute.

8. Dad keeps his _____ on a hook near the door.

Sequencing

Directions Finish each sentence. Use the words **before** or **after**.

1. I brush my teeth _____ I go to sleep.

2. I eat breakfast _____ I go to school.

3. I put on my shoes _____ I put on my socks.

4. I answer the phone _____ it rings.

5. I put the stamp on the letter _____
I mailed it.

Sequence

Directions Think of something you did this morning. Write two
sentences about what you did using the words *before* and *after*.

_____

_____

_____

_____

Name _____

Plural Nouns

Directions Circle the plural nouns in the sentences below.

1. Maria is 2 inches taller than Suri.

2. We have to clean up our own messes.

3. My grandmother gives me lots of kisses.

4. Dad used matches to light the fire.

5. Juan's pets are very playful.

Directions Write the plural form of the words in the box in the sentences below.

lunch	band	boss

6. Mom packed our _____ in brown paper bags.

7. My dad's _____ are very nice people.

8. All of the _____ played well.

Produce Language

My Weekly Concept Journal

Directions Write your answers in the space provided.

Day 1 _____
_____
_____
_____

Day 2 _____
_____
_____
_____

Day 3 _____
_____
_____
_____

Day 4 _____
_____
_____
_____

Name _____

Produce Language

My Weekly Concept Journal

Directions Write 2 or 3 sentences to answer the weekly question.

Why is it a good idea to work together?

_____

_____

_____

_____

_____

_____

_____

_____

_____

_____

_____

_____

_____

_____

_____

_____

_____

_____

_____

Solving Problems

Vocabulary

door	difficult	minute
table	explained	

Directions Finish the sentences. Use words from the box.

1. Celia knocked on the bedroom _____.

2. She needed help with a _____ math problem.

3. There was a clock on the _____.

4. Her mother _____ that it was broken.

5. The _____ hand did not move.

_____

Directions Use three words from above in sentences of your own. Use these sentence starters if you need help.
A clock... **The teacher...** **My friends and I...**

6. _____

_____

7. _____

_____

8. _____

_____

Name _____

/ā/ Spelled a, ai, ay

Directions Write the word that names the picture. Use these words: **baby, crayon, paints, rain.**

1. _____

2.  _____

3. _____

4. _____

Directions Finish these sentences. Use the words you wrote above.

5. Marco has a new set of _____.

6. Mom took an umbrella in case of _____.

7. My family has a new _____.

8. I broke my red _____.

Name _____

Comparing

Directions Look at these two wagons. Finish the sentences.
Use the words **full** and **empty.**

1. This wagon is _____ .

2. This wagon is _____ .

Comparing

Directions Look at the wagons above. Write two sentences that
compare the wagons.

3. The wagons are alike because

_____

_____ .

4. The wagons are different because

_____

_____ .

Name _____

Possessive Nouns

Directions Read the sentences. Circle the possessive nouns.

1. Lina's scarf is blue.

2. We helped wash Dad's car.

3. The dog ate the cat's food.

4. I borrowed David's sled.

5. My grandmother's house is painted white.

_____

Directions Write two sentences using possessive nouns.

6. _____

_____

7. _____

_____

Name _____

Produce Language

My Weekly Concept Journal

Directions Write your answers in the space provided.

Day 1 _____
_____
_____
_____
_____

Day 2 _____
_____
_____
_____
_____
_____

Day 3 _____
_____
_____
_____
_____

Day 4 _____
_____
_____
_____
_____

Name _____

Produce Language

My Weekly Concept Journal

Directions Write 2 or 3 sentences to answer the weekly question.

How can we work together to solve problems?

_____

_____

_____

_____

_____

_____

_____

_____

_____

_____

_____

_____

_____

_____

_____

_____

_____

_____

Name _____

Helping People in Danger

Directions Write the letter of the phrase that gives the meaning of each word.

1. _____ family

2. _____ firefighter

3. _____ dangerous

4. _____ listen

A. a person whose job is to stop fires

B. to pay attention to what someone is saying or to something that you hear

C. a group of people who are related to each other, such as moms and dads and children

D. able or likely to harm you

The /är/ and /ôr/ Sounds

The /är/ sound is made by the letters *ar*. The /ôr/ sound is made by the letters *or*.

Directions Write the letters **ar** or **or** to finish each word.

5.

c __ __ n

6.

y __ __ n

7.

st __ __

Name _____

Sequencing/Sequence

Sequence is the order of events. Special words such as *first*, *next*, and *last* tell the sequence.

Directions Write the order of the sentences. Use **1, 2,** and **3.**

Next, he lifted the kitten out of the tree. _____
Last, he handed the kitten to the girl. _____
First, the firefighter climbed his ladder. _____

Nouns

Nouns name people, places, and things.

Directions Finish the sentences. Use these words:
firefighter, boots, station.

1. Being a _____ is an important job.

2. Our class visited the fire _____.

3. We saw the firefighters' coats and _____.

Think, Talk, and Write

Directions Reread **Helping People in Danger** and **Fire Plan** on Student Worktext pages 54–55.

4. Talk about helping others with a partner. Read your Weekly Concept Journal on page 50. Change or add to what you wrote.

Changing History

Directions Write the letter of the phrase that gives the meaning of each word.

1. _____ hurricane

A. harm that has been done to something

2. _____ rebuild

B. a dangerous storm with very strong, fast winds

3. _____ damage

C. could not

4. _____ great

D. to repair or make like new again

5. _____ worst

E. very good

6. _____ couldn't

F. worse than anything else

Contractions

A **contraction** is a short way to say or write two words.

Directions Write the words as contractions.

7. is not _____

9. was not _____

8. what is _____

10. she will _____

Name _____

Describing/Author's Purpose

When we **describe,** we tell how a person looks, acts, or feels. Words that describe can help you figure out the **author's purpose** for writing.

Directions Read the sentences. Circle the verbs. Underline the describing words.

1. Jokes are funny.

2. That mask is scary.

3. Movies are exciting.

Proper Nouns

A **proper noun** names a person, place, or thing, and begins with a capital letter.

Directions Finish the sentences. Use these proper nouns: **Anna, San Diego, Chen.**

4. My sister's name is _____.

5. _____ helped me fix my bike.

6. Juan lives in _____.

Think, Talk, and Write

Directions Reread **Changing History** and **Rebuilding** on Student Worktext pages 60–61.

7. Talk about working together with a partner. Read your Weekly Concept Journal on page 56. Change or add to what you wrote.

Meeting Needs

Directions Write the letter of the phrase that gives the meaning of each word.

1. _____ tools   **A.** as much as needed

2. _____ enough   **B.** to do a job

3. _____ whole   **C.** complete

4. _____ work   **D.** things that help you build or repair

The /ėr/ Sound

You can write the /ėr/ sound with the letters **er, ir,** or **ur.**

Directions Finish the words. Use **er, ir,** or **ur.**

5.   b___ ___d

6.   f___ ___n

7.   n___ ___se

Name _____

Asking Questions/Author's Purpose

The words *who, what,* and *where* are clue words for **asking questions.** Sometimes the **author's purpose** is to answer a question.

Directions Read **What Do You Need to Make a Garden?** on page 69 of your Student Worktext. Why do you think the author wrote it?

_____

_____

Singular and Plural Nouns

A **singular noun** names one person, place, or thing. A **plural noun** names more than one person, place, or thing.

Directions Read the sentences. Circle the singular nouns. Underline the plural nouns.

1. This garden is beautiful.

2. There are a lot of flowers.

3. The sun is warm.

Think, Talk, and Write

Directions Reread **Meeting Needs** and **A Garden Grows!** on Student Worktext pages 66–67.

4. Talk about working together to meet people's needs with a partner. Read your Weekly Concept Journal on page 62. Change or add to what you wrote.

Working Together

Directions Write the letter of the phrase that gives the meaning of each word.

1. _____ band   **A.** a group of people who play

                        music together

2. _____ instruments   **B.** likely to happen or to be true

3. _____ people   **C.** to form pictures and ideas in your mind

4. _____ imagine   **D.** more than one person

5. _____ probably   **E.** things used to make music

Adding -*s*, -*es*, -*ies*

When you add -*s*, -*es*, or -*ies* to a word, you make it plural. If the word ends with -*y*, you make it plural by changing the -*y* to an *i* and adding -*es*.

Directions Write the plural form of each word.

6. fly _____

7. face _____

8. fox _____

Name _____

Sequencing/Sequence

Sequence is the order of events. The words *before* and *after* help us tell when things happen.

Directions Think of something you did yesterday. Write two sentences about it. Use the words *before* and *after*.

1. _____

2. _____

Plural Nouns

A **plural noun** names more than one person, place, or thing.

Directions Write the plural form of each word.

3. beach _____   5. ditch _____

4. bus _____   6. boss _____

Think, Talk, and Write

Directions Reread **Working Together** and **Playing in a Band** on Student Worktext pages 72–73.

7. Talk with a partner about working together. Read your Weekly Concept Journal on page 68. Change or add to what you wrote.

Solving Problems

Directions Write the letter of the phrase that gives the meaning of each word.

1. _____ door

A. made something easy to understand

2. _____ table

B. a piece of flat wood or metal with four legs

3. _____ difficult

C. the flat piece of wood or metal that you push or pull to go into a room

4. _____ explained

D. an amount of time equal to 60 seconds

5. _____ minute

E. not easy to do or understand

/ā/ Spelled *a*, *ai*, and *ay*

You can write the long *a* sound with the letters **a, ai,** and **ay.**

Directions Finish the words that name the picture. Use **a, ai,** or **ay.**

6. st _____ n

7. tr _____ n

8. tr _____

9.  c _____ ne

Name _____

Comparing

We are **comparing** when we tell about how things are alike and different.

Directions Look at these two pictures. Write two sentences that compare the pictures.

1. The pictures are alike because _____.

2. The pictures are different because _____.

Possessive Nouns

A **possessive noun** names a person, place, or thing that owns something. You can change a noun to a possessive noun by adding 's.

Directions Read the sentences. Circle the possessive nouns.

3. I found Marco's ball.

4. The child's toy is broken.

5. Jan's father is a police officer.

Think, Talk, and Write

Directions Reread **Solving Problems** and **Homework Helpers** on Student Worktext pages 78–79.

6. Talk about solving problems with a partner. Read your Weekly Concept Journal on page 74. Change or add to what you wrote.

Helping with Creative Ideas

Vocabulary

buckets	creative	village
river	pretty	

Directions Finish the sentences. Use words from the box.

1. Juan lived in a _____ .

2. It was a _____ place to live.

3. People used water from a _____ .

4. Juan had a _____ idea.

5. They used _____ to carry the water.

Directions Use three words from above in sentences of your own. Use these sentence starters if you need help.

Juan lives...   **Juan had a...**   **You can carry water...**

6. _____

_____

7. _____

_____

8. _____

_____

Name _____

The Sound /ē/

Directions Write the word that names the picture. Use words from the box.

beach	city	heel	sunny	wheel

1. _____

2. _____

3. _____

4. _____

5. _____

Directions Finish the sentences. Use the new words you wrote above.

6. Ivan lived in a big _____.

7. It was a _____ day.

8. Clara wanted to swim at the _____.

9. The _____ on the wagon was broken.

10. Julio had a blister on his _____.

Name _____

Comparing

Directions Finish the sentences. Use these words:
book, like, hat.

1. Irma is tall. Julia is tall. Irma is _____ Julia.

2. My coat is blue. My hat is blue. My coat is like my

_____ .

3. The book is heavy. The bag is heavy. The _____ is

like the bag.

Compare and Contrast

Directions Look at the pictures and read the sentences.
Then finish the sentences.

The tiger is a cat. It has stripes.

The lion is a cat. It has a mane.

4. A tiger is like a lion because _____

_____ .

5. A tiger is not like a lion because _____

_____ .

Name _____

Verbs

Directions Circle the verbs in each sentence below.

1. We eat lunch at school.

2. Laura rides her bike to the park.

3. Mark sings with the school chorus.

4. They swim at the pool.

5. Linda helps her little sister.

Directions Finish the sentences. Use these words:
pulls, fills, jumps, cooks, talks.

6. Oscar _____ on the phone.

7. Sara _____ the bucket with water.

8. Carlo _____ over the puddle.

9. Tina _____ the wagon up a hill.

10. Pedro _____ dinner with his dad.

Produce Language

My Weekly Concept Journal

Directions Write your answers in the space provided.

Day 1 _____

_____

_____

_____

Day 2 _____

_____

_____

_____

Day 3 _____

_____

_____

_____

Day 4 _____

_____

_____

_____

Name _____

Produce Language

My Weekly Concept Journal

Directions Write 2 or 3 sentences to answer the weekly question.

When does support from others help with a creative idea?

_____

_____

_____

_____

_____

_____

_____

_____

_____

_____

_____

_____

_____

_____

_____

_____

_____

_____

Sharing Ideas

Vocabulary

artist	water lilies	paint
sunrise	communicate	show

Directions Finish the sentences. Use words from the box.

1. _____ are flowers that grow in ponds and lakes.

2. Monet was an _____ .

3. Anna got up early in the morning to see the _____ .

4. People _____ their ideas in many ways.

5. Louis wants to _____ a picture of the tree.

6. Cats _____ they are happy when they purr.

Directions Use three words from above in sentences of your own. Use these sentence starters if you need help.

Red...   People can...   Monet made pictures of...

7. _____

_____

8. _____

_____

9. _____

_____

Name _____

The Sound /ō/

Directions Write the word that names the picture. Use words from the box.

bow	bowl	coat	gold

1. _____

2. _____

3. _____

4. _____

___

Directions Finish the sentences. Use the words you wrote above.

5. Lee put on his hat and _____.

6. The ring was made of _____.

7. Maria had a _____ of soup.

8. The gift was in a box with a big _____.

Name _____

Interpreting

Directions Look at this picture.
Tell what you think it communicates.

1. I think the picture shows _____

_____ .

Draw Conclusions

Directions Reread **Painting** on page 93 of your Student
Worktext. Draw a conclusion with a partner.

2. I think Monet _____

_____ .

Name _____

Nouns and Verbs

Directions Circle the verbs and draw a line under the nouns in the sentences below.

1. Artists paint pictures.

2. Maria picks flowers.

3. My friends swim in the lake.

4. Raymond ran to the store.

Directions Finish the sentences. Write a verb in the blanks below.

5. Juan _____ a picture.

6. Abdul _____ to school.

7. The cat _____ up onto the chair.

8. Erika _____ in a race.

Produce Language

My Weekly Concept Journal

Directions Write your answers in the space provided.

Day 1 _____
_____
_____
_____
_____

Day 2 _____
_____
_____
_____
_____
_____

Day 3 _____
_____
_____
_____
_____

Day 4 _____
_____
_____
_____
_____
_____

Name _____

Produce Language

My Weekly Concept Journal

Directions Write 2 or 3 sentences to answer the weekly question.

In what creative ways do we communicate?

_____

_____

_____

_____

_____

_____

_____

_____

_____

_____

_____

_____

_____

_____

_____

_____

_____

_____

Creative Ways to Solve Problems

Vocabulary

suitcases	heavy	today
wheels	solve	whatever

Directions Finish the sentences. Use words from the box.

1. _____ is Monday.

2. Lea can _____ that math problem.

3. The big box was too _____ to carry.

4. People take _____ when they travel.

5. I can buy _____ I want at the store.

6. A bicycle has two _____ .

Directions Use two words from above in sentences of your own. Use these sentence starters if you need help.
Creative thinking...   I buy...

7. _____

_____

_____

8. _____

_____

Name _____

Compound Words

Directions Fill in the blanks to finish each compound word.
Use these words: **bee**, **meal**, **rain**, **hay**, **plane**.

1.   _____ stack

2.   air _____

3. _____ bow

4. _____ hive

5.   oat _____

Directions Finish the sentences. Use the compound words
you made above.

6. Alicia likes _____ for breakfast.

7. An _____ lands at the airport.

8. Julia looked up and saw a _____ in the sky.

9. There is a _____ in that tree.

10. You can see a _____ at the farm.

Name _____

Cause-and-Effect Relationship

Directions Look at the picture. Tell
what happened and why it happened.
Use the word *because*.

_____

_____

Cause and Effect

Directions Read the sentences. Circle the cause. Draw a line
under the effect.

1. Grace rolled the suitcase because it was heavy.

2. Mom took an umbrella because it was raining.

3. We went to the store because we were out of milk.

4. There is no school today because it is Saturday.

Name _____

Verbs

Directions Circle the verbs in the sentences below.

1. Mark watched a movie.

2. Lee takes a cookie.

3. We will go to the beach tomorrow.

4. Yesterday, I played soccer.

5. Claire wants a teddy bear for her birthday.

Directions Tell whether each sentence happened in the **past,** is happening in the **present,** or will happen in the **future.**

6. Roberta picks flowers at the park. _____

7. Pam picked a flower for her mom. _____

8. Mrs. Wen will pick flowers from her garden. _____

Name _____

Produce Language

My Weekly Concept Journal

Directions Write your answers in the space provided.

Day 1 _____
_____
_____
_____

Day 2 _____
_____
_____
_____

Day 3 _____
_____
_____
_____

Day 4 _____
_____
_____
_____

Name _____

Produce Language

My Weekly Concept Journal

Directions Write 2 or 3 sentences to answer the weekly question.

How can creative thinking solve a problem?

_____

_____

_____

_____

_____

_____

_____

_____

_____

_____

_____

_____

_____

_____

_____

_____

_____

Surprising Ideas

Vocabulary

sculpture	tiger	many
stone	instead	surprised

Directions Finish the sentences. Use the words in the box.

1. There are _____ animals at the zoo.

2. Paul saw a _____ at the zoo.

3. An artist made a _____.

4. She made it out of _____.

5. The ending of the movie _____ us.

6. Rosa walked home _____ of taking the bus.

Directions Use two words from above in sentences of your own. Use these sentence starters if you need help.

At the zoo...   An artist...

7. _____

_____

8. _____

_____

Name _____

The Sound /ī/

Directions Write the word that names the picture. Use words from the box.

child	fly	light	pie

1. _____

2. _____

3. _____

4. _____

Directions Finish the sentences. Use the words you wrote above.

5. I turned on the _____ .

6. Mom baked an apple _____ .

7. There was a _____ on the wall.

8. The babysitter watched the _____ .

Making Predictions

Directions Look at the picture. What do you think is going to happen?

_____

_____

Theme and Plot

Directions Look at the pictures. What is the big idea? What might the boy do next?

1. The big idea is _____

_____.

2. The boy might _____

_____.

Name _____

Verbs

Directions Circle the verbs in the sentences below.

1. Nancy painted a picture of a tree.

2. Ethan will go to art camp this summer.

3. Ella sees her friend on the bus.

4. I will visit my grandparents.

5. Pam walked to school.

_____

Directions Write about something you did yesterday. Write about something you will do tomorrow.

6. Yesterday, I _____

_____ .

7. Tomorrow, I _____

_____ .

Produce Language

My Weekly Concept Journal

Directions Write your answers in the space provided.

Day 1 _____

_____

_____

_____

_____

Day 2 _____

_____

_____

_____

_____

Day 3 _____

_____

_____

_____

_____

Day 4 _____

_____

_____

_____

_____

Name _____

Produce Language

My Weekly Concept Journal

Directions Write 2 or 3 sentences to answer the weekly question.

When does a creative idea lead to a surprise?

_____

_____

_____

_____

_____

_____

_____

_____

_____

_____

_____

_____

_____

_____

_____

_____

_____

_____

The Start of Ideas

Vocabulary

burrs	touch fastener	hours
clothes	easier	invent

Directions Finish the sentences. Use words from the box.

1. We walked for _____ .

2. _____ stuck to the dog's fur.

3. George had an idea about a new thing to _____ .

4. A _____ holds two things together.

5. It is _____ to use than buttons or a zipper.

6. Many shoes and _____ use them.

Directions Use two words from above in sentences of your own. Use these sentence starters if you need help.

A creative idea...   Some games...

7. _____

_____

8. _____

_____

Name _____

Comparative Endings

Directions Add the comparative endings **-er** and **-est** to each word.

Base word	-er	-est
funny		
big		
gentle		

Directions Finish the sentences. Use the new words you wrote above.

1. That is the _____ joke I ever heard.

2. A lion is _____ than a cat.

3. A cat is _____ than a lion.

4. Elephants are the _____ animals at the zoo.

5. I use my _____ touch when I hold the baby.

6. That book is _____ than the one I read last week.

Cause-and-Effect Relationship

Directions Finish each sentence to tell *why* something happened.

1. Cho changed her shirt _____ .

2. Mike got a present _____ .

3. I wore boots _____ .

4. Angela went swimming

_____ .

Cause and Effect

Directions Read the sentences. Tell the cause and effect.

5. The glass broke because it fell off the table.

Cause: _____

Effect: _____

6. Carla could not play outside because it was raining.

Cause: _____

Effect: _____

Name _____

Verbs

Directions Circle the verb in each sentence.

1. George is an inventor.

2. I am at an art show.

3. My grandparents were here yesterday.

4. I was sleepy.

5. We are on the roller coaster.

Directions Finish each sentence. Use a verb.

6. Yesterday, I _____ sick.

7. Today, I _____ feeling better.

8. We _____ happy that our cousins came to visit.

9. They _____ homesick, but they are not now.

Produce Language

My Weekly Concept Journal

Directions Write your answers in the space provided.

Day 1 _____

_____

_____

_____

Day 2 _____

_____

_____

_____

_____

Day 3 _____

_____

_____

_____

_____

Day 4 _____

_____

_____

_____

_____

Name _____

Produce Language

My Weekly Concept Journal

Directions Write 2 or 3 sentences to answer the weekly question.

Where do creative ideas come from?

_____

_____

_____

_____

_____

_____

_____

_____

_____

_____

_____

_____

_____

_____

_____

_____

_____

_____

_____

Helping with Creative Ideas

Directions Write the letter of the phrase that gives the meaning of each word.

1. ____ buckets   **A.** a very small town

2. ____ river   **B.** good at making new and interesting things

3. ____ creative   **C.** big containers that can hold water

4. ____ pretty   **D.** nice to look at

5. ____ village   **E.** a long body of water that goes into an ocean or a lake

The Sound /ē/

The long e sound says its name.

Directions Finish the sentences. Use these words: **city, behind, even.**

6. Two, four, and six are _____ numbers.

7. I live in a _____ .

8. I found my book _____ the chair.

Name _____

Comparing/Compare and Contrast

When we **compare**, we tell how things are alike. When we **contrast**, we tell how they are different.

Directions Finish the sentences. Use the words **like** and **not like.**

1. A fly is small. An ant is small. A fly is _____ an ant.

2. An ant is small. An elephant is big. An ant is _____ an elephant.

Verbs

A **verb** can be an action word.

Directions Finish the sentences. Use a verb.

3. Olivia _____ softball.

4. Tito _____ the bucket filled with water.

Think, Talk, and Write

Directions Reread **Helping with Creative Ideas** and **The River** on Student Worktext pages 86–87.

5. Talk about getting help with creative ideas with a partner. Read your Weekly Concept Journal on page 90. Change or add to what you wrote.

Sharing Ideas

Directions Write the letter of the phrase that gives the meaning of each word.

1. _____ artist

A. plants with leaves and flowers that live in water

2. _____ sunrise

B. someone who paints or draws pictures

3. _____ water lilies

C. to let someone see something

4. _____ communicate

D. to speak or write to someone

5. _____ paint

E. to put a colored liquid on a surface

6. _____ show

F. the time in the morning when the sun first comes up

The Sound /ō/

The long o sound says its name.

Directions Finish the sentences. Use these words:
fold, float, odor.

7. I help _____ the clean sheets.

8. A bad smell is also called an _____.

9. A leaf will _____ on water.

Name _____

Interpreting/Draw Conclusions

Interpreting is telling what you think something means. When you **draw conclusions,** you use what you read, see, or know to tell about something.

Directions Look at this picture. Tell what you think it communicates.

1. I think this picture shows _____.

Nouns and Verbs

A **noun** names a person, place, or thing. A **verb** can show action.

Directions Circle the verbs and draw a line under the nouns in the sentences below.

2. Kia writes a letter.

3. Luis swims in his pool.

Think, Talk, and Write

Directions Reread **Sharing Ideas** and **Painting** on Student Worktext pages 92–93.

4. Talk about how we can communicate in creative ways with a partner. Read your Weekly Concept Journal on page 96. Change or add to what you wrote.

Creative Ways to Solve Problems

Directions Write the letter of the phrase that gives the meaning of each word.

1. ____ suitcases

A. round things under something that turn around and allow it to move

2. ____ wheels

B. to find the answer

3. ____ heavy

C. any or all of the things that are needed or wanted

4. ____ solve

D. large bags used to carry clothes

5. ____ today

E. the day it is now

6. ____ whatever

F. weighing a lot

Compound Words

A **compound word** is made up of two words joined together.

Directions Put the words together. Write a sentence with the compound word.

7. day + light _____

Sentence: _____

8. pea + nut _____

Sentence: _____

Name _____

Cause-and-Effect Relationship/ Cause and Effect

A **cause** is why something happens. An **effect** is what happens, or the result.

Directions Look at the picture. Tell what happened and why it happened. Use the word *because*.

1. _____

_____

Verbs

A **verb** can tell an action. Verbs can tell about an action in the past, present, or future.

Directions Tell if each sentence happened in the **past,** is happening in the **present,** or will happen in the **future.**

2. Fatina will visit her grandmother. _____

3. Ken visited a friend. _____

Think, Talk, and Write

Directions Reread **Creative Ways to Solve Problems** and **Suitcases** on Student Worktext pages 98–99.

4. Talk with a partner about how creative thinking can solve a problem. Read your Weekly Concept Journal on page 102. Change or add to what you wrote.

Surprising Ideas

Directions Write the letter of the phrase that gives the meaning of each word.

1. _____ sculpture

A. a smooth piece of rock

2. _____ stone

B. in place of

3. _____ tiger

C. saw something that was new or not expected

4. _____ instead

D. an object made from wood, stone, or metal

5. _____ surprised

E. a large, strong wild cat that has yellow fur with black stripes

The Sound /ī/

The long *i* sound says its name.

Directions Finish the sentences. Use these words:
high, silent, diver.

6. A _____ can stay underwater for a long time.

7. It was _____ before the movie started.

8. I can't reach the _____ shelf.

Name _____

Making Predictions/Theme and Plot

When we **make predictions**, we tell about something we think will happen in the future. A **plot** is what happens in a story. A **theme** is the big idea.

Directions Look at the picture. What do you think is going to happen?

_____

Verbs

We can use **verbs** to tell what happened in the past, what is happening now, and what will happen in the future.

Directions Finish the sentences. Use the correct tense of the verb *paint*.

1. Yesterday, Vera _____ a picture of a tree in art class.

2. Tomorrow, we _____ a picture of a frog.

Think, Talk, and Write

Directions Reread **Surprising Ideas** and **The Sculpture** on Student Worktext pages 104–105.

3. Talk with a partner about how a creative idea can lead to a surprise. Read your Weekly Concept Journal on page 108. Change or add to what you wrote.

The Start of Ideas

Directions Write the letter of the phrase that gives the meaning of each word.

1. _____ burrs

A. amounts of time, each equal to 60 minutes

2. _____ clothes

B. two pieces of fabric that stick together

3. _____ touch fastener

C. the prickly coverings of some fruits and seeds that cling to things

4. _____ easier

D. to think of an idea, or to make something for the first time

5. _____ hours

E. less difficult

6. _____ invent

F. the things that you wear on your body

Comparative Endings

We use the ending *-er* to compare two things. We use the ending *-est* to compare more than two things.

Directions Write the new word.

7. safe + -er = _____

8. easy + -er = _____

9. friendly + -er = _____

10. hot + -est = _____

Name _____

Cause-and-Effect Relationship/ Cause and Effect

A **cause** is why something happens. An **effect** is what happens, or the result. We use special words, such as *because*, to tell why.

Directions Read the sentence. Tell the cause and effect.

1. Mom got angry because we broke her vase.

Cause: _____

Effect: _____

Verbs

Verbs can tell what happens in the present. Verbs can also tell what happened in the past.

Directions Finish the sentences. Use a verb.

2. I _____ excited about the party.

3. They _____ happy to see their friends.

4. It _____ cold today.

Think, Talk, and Write

Directions Reread **The Start of Ideas** and **A Creative Idea** on Student Worktext pages 110–111.

5. Talk with a partner about where creative ideas come from. Read your Weekly Concept Journal on page 114. Change or add to what you wrote.

Name _____

Life Changes

Vocabulary

bundle	strange
quilt	wrapped

Directions Finish the sentences. Use words from the box.

1. Ana moved to a _____ new place.

2. The _____ gift looked pretty.

3. Inside was a _____ tied up with a ribbon.

4. She put the new _____ on her bed.

Directions Use three vocabulary words in sentences of your own. Use these sentence starters if you need help.

New places...   The gift...   Family things...

5. _____

_____

6. _____

_____

7. _____

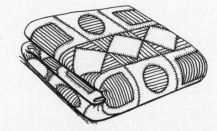

_____

Name _____

Consonant + -*le*

Directions Draw a line to show how these words break into two syllables.

1.   bundle

2.   candle

3.   bugle

4.   table

Directions Finish the sentences. Use the words from above.

5. He put the glass down on the _____.

6. He used string to tie the sticks into a _____.

7. She blew out all but one _____ on the birthday cake.

8. Martin plays the _____ in his school band.

Comparing and Contrasting

Directions Complete each sentence.

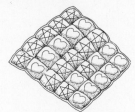 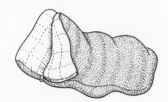

1. _____ is like _____ because _____ .

2. _____ is unlike _____ because _____ .

3. _____ is like _____ because _____ .

4. _____ is unlike _____ because _____ .

Compare and Contrast

Directions Tell how the animals are alike.
Tell how they are different.

5. The animals are like each other because _____

_____ .

6. The animals are unlike each other because _____

_____ .

Adjectives

Directions Read the sentences. Circle the adjectives.

1. She is making a red quilt.

2. I live in a tall building.

3. He is a happy boy.

4. It was a cold day.

5. Grandma has white hair.

Directions Finish each sentence. Use an adjective from the box.

hot	happy	long
sad	small	blue

6. It is a _____ cat.

7. He is a _____ boy.

8. She is a _____ girl.

9. He has a _____ pot.

10. She has _____ hair.

Name _____

Produce Language

My Weekly Concept Journal

Directions Write your answers in the space provided.

Day 1 _____

_____

_____

_____

Day 2 _____

_____

_____

_____

Day 3 _____

_____

_____

_____

Day 4 _____

_____

_____

_____

_____

Name _____

Produce Language

My Weekly Concept Journal

Directions Write 2 or 3 sentences to answer the weekly question.

How can familiar things help us with changes?

_____

_____

_____

_____

_____

_____

_____

_____

_____

_____

_____

_____

_____

_____

_____

_____

_____

_____

Plant Changes

Vocabulary

blossoms	**autumn**	**seed**
soil	**harvest**	

Directions Finish the sentences. Use the words in the box.

1. A big plant can grow from a tiny _____ .

2. Plants need water and good _____ to grow.

3. Apple trees have pretty _____ in the spring.

4. Some trees lose their leaves in _____ .

5. These apples are ripe and ready to _____ .

Directions Use two words from above in sentences of your own. Use these sentence starters if you need help.

Apple trees...   Plants grow...

6. _____

_____

7. _____

_____

Name _____

The Sound /u̇/ Spelled *oo* and *u*

Directions Write the word that names the picture.

1.  _____

2.  _____

3. _____

4. _____

Directions Finish the sentences. Use the words you wrote above.

5. I _____ my sister in the wagon.

6. There is a _____ in the field with the cows.

7. Her _____ is too big for that shoe.

8. I read that _____ before.

Describing

Directions Circle the describing words.

1. We picked red apples.

2. The trees were big.

3. The trees were planted in neat rows.

4. We looked up at the blue sky.

5. We made sweet applesauce.

Details and Facts

Directions Read each sentence. Add a detail.

Apple trees bloom in spring.

6. The blossoms are _____.

Apples are ready to harvest in autumn.

7. The apples are _____.

Name _____

Adjectives

Directions Circle the adjectives in each sentence. Some sentences have two adjectives.

1. She has three apples.

2. These red grapes are sweet.

3. Look at that big tree.

4. It has pink blossoms.

5. The tree has small green leaves.

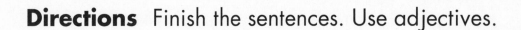

Directions Finish the sentences. Use adjectives.

6. I have _____ socks.

7. My shirt is _____ .

8. My shoes are _____ .

9. My pants are _____ .

Produce Language

My Weekly Concept Journal

Directions Write your answers in the space provided.

Day 1 _____

_____

_____

_____

Day 2 _____

_____

_____

_____

Day 3 _____

_____

_____

_____

Day 4 _____

_____

_____

_____

Name _____

Produce Language

My Weekly Concept Journal

Directions Write 2 or 3 sentences to answer the weekly question.

How do plants change over time?

_____

_____

_____

_____

_____

_____

_____

_____

_____

_____

_____

_____

_____

_____

_____

_____

_____

_____

Changes Under the Ground

Vocabulary

badger	burrow	underground
claws	tunnels	

Directions Finish the sentences. Use the words from the box.

1. A _____ is a small wild animal.

2. They have sharp _____ on their feet.

3. They dig _____ that go down into the ground.

4. They sleep in a _____ .

5. It is dark _____ .

_____

Directions Use two words from above in sentences of your own. Use these sentence starters if you need help.

Wild animals...   A badger...

6. _____

_____

7. _____

_____

Name _____

Diphthongs *ou* and *ow* Pronounced /ou/

Directions Circle the words that have the same vowel sound as the word *town*.

sour	cloud	how
about	pillow	out
throw	ground	yellow

Directions Circle the word that finishes the sentence.

1. He found/friend his lost mitten under his bed.

2. She put on an evening gone/gown to wear to the fancy party.

3. They planted seeds in the grind/ground.

4. We took the bus into town/twin.

Describing

Directions Circle the words that tell *where*.

1. The paper is under the book.

2. The word list is above the wall map.

3. The shelf is below the ceiling.

4. The light is above the desk.

5. The pencil is under the table.

Graphic Sources

Directions Finish the sentences. Use the graphic source to help you.

6. The stem is _____ the ground.

7. The root is _____ the ground.

8. The seeds are _____ the leaves.

9. The leaf is _____ the flower.

10. The flower is _____ the stem.

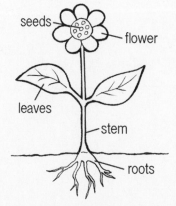

seeds — flower

leaves — stem

roots

Name _____

Adjectives That Compare

Directions Add -er and -est to the words. Write the new words.

1. tall + er _____   **3.** small + er _____

tall + est _____   small + est _____

2. long + er _____   **4.** fast + er _____

long + est _____   fast + est _____

_____

Directions Circle the word that finishes the sentence.

5. Dad is taller/tallest than Mom.

6. That is the smaller/smallest kitten I ever saw.

7. She has the longer/longest hair of any girl in our class.

8. He can run faster/fastest than his friends.

Produce Language

My Weekly Concept Journal

Directions Write your answers in the space provided.

Day 1 _____

_____

_____

_____

_____

Day 2 _____

_____

_____

_____

_____

Day 3 _____

_____

_____

_____

_____

Day 4 _____

_____

_____

_____

_____

Name _____

Produce Language

My Weekly Concept Journal

Directions Write 2 or 3 sentences to answer the weekly question.

What changes occur under the ground?

_____

_____

_____

_____

_____

_____

_____

_____

_____

_____

_____

_____

_____

_____

_____

_____

_____

_____

New Changes

Vocabulary

town	attend	fair
unhappy	enjoy	move

Directions Finish the sentences. Use the words in the box.

1. Ben and his sister like living in their _____ .

2. They _____ the same school.

3. They _____ going to the park.

4. Soon the family will _____ to a new place.

5. The children are _____ .

6. They think this isn't _____ to them.

Directions Use two words from above in sentences of your own. Use these sentence starters if you need help.

The family...   The new boy...

7. _____

_____

8. _____

_____

Name _____

The Sound /oi/

Directions Write the word that names the picture.

1. _ _ _

2. _ _ _

3. _ _ _ _

4. _ _ _ _

5. _ _ _ _

Directions Finish the sentences. Use the new words you wrote above.

6. He put the _____ in his piggy bank.

7. We planted the seeds in _____ .

8. There is a new _____ at school.

9. He covered the food with _____ .

10. She plays with the _____ .

Name _____

Describing

Directions Use the action word in parentheses to describe.

1. (move) The family is _____.

2. (walk) The girls are _____.

3. (play) The boys are _____.

4. (jump) The frog is _____.

5. (sleep) The cat is _____.

Plot

Directions Look at the pictures. They tell a story.
Write sentences that tell the plot.

Beginning: _____

Middle: _____

End: _____

Name _____

Adverbs

Directions Read the sentences. Circle the adverbs that tell *when* or *where*.

1. I got to school early.

2. My seat is here.

3. We have a field trip tomorrow.

4. The bus is late.

5. We live in the apartment above the Smiths.

Directions Finish the sentences. Use these adverbs:
yesterday, there, here, soon, above.

6. I live _____ .

7. The bus is leaving _____ .

8. We went to school _____ .

9. The park is _____ .

10. The clouds are _____ us.

Produce Language

My Weekly Concept Journal

Directions Write your answers in the space provided.

Day 1 _____

_____

_____

_____

_____

Day 2 _____

_____

_____

_____

_____

Day 3 _____

_____

_____

_____

_____

Day 4 _____

_____

_____

_____

_____

Name _____

Produce Language

My Weekly Concept Journal

Directions Write 2 or 3 sentences to answer the weekly question.

Why are some changes difficult?

_____
_____
_____
_____
_____
_____
_____
_____
_____
_____
_____
_____
_____
_____
_____
_____
_____
_____
_____
_____

Weather Changes

Vocabulary

branches	outside	weather
picnic	soon	

Directions Finish the sentences. Use the words in the box.

1. My family likes to do things _____.

2. The _____ is sunny and warm.

3. We are having a _____.

4. I see a kite stuck in the _____ of a tree.

5. _____ it will be time to go home.

Directions Use three words from above in sentences of your own. Use these sentence starters if you need help.
It is fun to...   Rain...   Trees...

6. _____

_____

7. _____

_____

8. _____

_____

Name _____

The Sound /ü/ Spelled *ew, ue, ui, oo*

Directions Circle the word that names the picture.

1.   zoo zip

2.  glue glow

3.   fruit fright

4.   moon main

5.   ream room

Directions Circle the word that finishes each sentence.

6. I will clean my roam/room after breakfast.

7. She lost two teeth and it is hard to chew/chin.

8. The dog finished its food/fund.

9. I got a now/new bike.

10. My father wears a suit/seat to work.

Evaluating

Directions Complete the sentences. Use **each** or **every.**

1. I picked up _____ toy in my room.

2. _____ child will get a turn.

3. I brush my teeth _____ night
before I go to bed.

4. I read _____ book on that shelf.

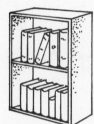

5. _____ coat is on sale.

Details and Facts

Directions Complete the sentences that tell details.

It rained yesterday.

6. Detail: The storm lasted all _____.

He has a new bike.

7. Detail: It is _____.

She lives in a big city.

8. Detail: There are a lot of _____.

Name _____

Adverbs

Directions Circle the adverbs that tell *how*.

1. He sings loudly.

2. They walk quickly.

3. The teacher writes neatly.

4. She asks politely.

5. She dances gracefully.

Directions Finish the sentences. Use an adverb.

6. They played together _____.

7. She pet the kitten _____.

8. He smiled _____.

9. They said good-bye _____.

10. She skated _____.

Name _____

Produce Language

My Weekly Concept Journal

Directions Write your answers in the space provided.

Day 1 _____

_____

_____

_____

Day 2 _____

_____

_____

_____

Day 3 _____

_____

_____

_____

Day 4 _____

_____

_____

_____

_____

Name _____

Produce Language

My Weekly Concept Journal

Directions Write 2 or 3 sentences to answer the weekly question:

How do changes in the weather affect us?

_____

_____

_____

_____

_____

_____

_____

_____

_____

_____

_____

_____

_____

_____

_____

_____

_____

_____

_____

Life Changes

Directions Write the letter of the phrase that gives the meaning of each word.

1. _____ bundle

A. a soft thick cover for a bed

2. _____ quilt

B. covered by something such as paper or cloth

3. _____ strange

C. a group of things such as papers or clothes that are tied together

4. _____ wrapped

D. unusual, surprising, or difficult to understand

Consonant + -*le*

Some words have more than one syllable. If a word ends in a **consonant** and the letters -*le*, those letters make up a syllable.

Directions Draw a line to break the words into two syllables.

5. circle

7. pebble

6. table

8. bundle

Name _____

Comparing and Contrasting/ Compare and Contrast

When you **compare,** you tell how things are alike. When you **contrast,** you tell how things are different.

Directions Write two sentences that compare or contrast a crayon and a pencil.

1. A crayon is like a pencil because _____.

2. A crayon is unlike a pencil because _____.

Adjectives

Words that describe nouns are called **adjectives.**

Directions Write an adjective to describe each picture.

3. _____   **4.** _____

Think, Talk, and Write

Directions Reread **Life Changes** and **Grandma's Surprise** on Student Worktext pages 118–119.

5. Talk with a partner about how family things can help us feel better about change. Read your Weekly Concept Journal on page 130. Change or add to what you wrote.

Plant Changes

Directions Write the letter of the phrase that gives the meaning of each word.

1. _____ blossoms

A. a small grain from which a new plant grows

2. _____ soil

B. to gather crops from the fields

3. _____ autumn

C. new flowers on a tree or bush

4. _____ harvest

D. the earth in which plants grow

5. _____ seed

E. the season between summer and winter

The Sound / u̇/ Spelled *oo* and *u*

The /u̇/ sound can be spelled two ways: *oo* or *u*.

Directions Circle the words with the same /u̇/ vowel sound as *wool* and *pull*.

push	bush	full	moon	tool
soon	mule	hood	cook	hoof

Name _____

Describing/Details and Facts

Facts are pieces of information that are true. **Details** can tell more about facts. We use **describing** words in details.

Directions Write details about a flower. Think about how it looks and smells. Use describing words in your details.

1. The flower is _____.

_____

Adjectives

An **adjective** gives a detail to describe a noun.

Directions Write an adjective to describe each picture.

2. _____   **3.** _____

_____

Think, Talk, and Write

Directions Reread **Plant Changes** and **Apple Trees** on Student Worktext pages 124–125.

4. Talk with a partner about how plants change and grow. Read your Weekly Concept Journal on page 136. Change or add to what you wrote.

Name _____

Changes Under the Ground

Directions Write the letter of the phrase that gives the meaning of each word.

1. ____ badger

2. ____ claws

3. ____ burrow

4. ____ tunnels

5. ____ underground

A. passages under the ground

B. a wild animal with black and white fur that lives in a hole

C. a hole in the ground made by a small animal

D. under the ground; under the earth's surface

E. hard sharp parts on the foot of an animal

Diphthongs *ou* and *ow* Pronounced /ou/

Words with different letter combinations can have the same sound. The **ow** in *clown* sounds like the **ou** in *found*.

Directions Circle the words with the same vowel sound as *clown* and *found*.

bounce	toy	grow	blow	bowl
shout	cow	crown	frown	round

Name _____

Describing/Graphic Sources

Graphic sources are pictures or diagrams that help you learn new things. You can use words such as *below*, *above*, and *under* to **describe** different parts of the diagram.

Directions Use the graphic source to finish the sentences.

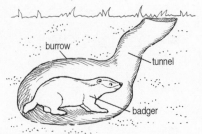

1. The burrow is _____ the ground.

2. The tunnel is _____ the burrow.

3. The ground is _____ the tunnel.

Adjectives That Compare

Adjectives that end in *-er* and *-est* are **adjectives that compare.**

Directions Add *-er* or *-est* to each adjective to complete the sentence correctly.

4. (sweet) A soft, ripe peach is _____ than a hard one.

5. (warm) Summer is the _____ time of year.

Think, Talk, and Write

Directions Reread **Changes Under the Ground** and **Underground Home** on Student Worktext pages 130–131.

6. Talk with a partner about changes underground. Read your Weekly Concept Journal on page 142. Change or add to what you wrote.

New Changes

Directions Write the letter of the phrase that gives the meaning of each word.

1. _____ town

2. _____ unhappy

3. _____ attend

4. _____ enjoy

5. _____ fair

6. _____ move

A. to go to or be at an event or class

B. to get pleasure and happiness from something

C. sad or worried; not happy

D. to go to a new place to live

E. a place with houses and stores where people live and work

F. equal for everyone

The Sound /oi/

The *oy* in *boy* sounds like the *oi* in *oil*.

Directions Circle the words with the same vowel sound as *boy* and *oil*.

coin	ton	join	spoil
toy	joy	story	spoon

Name _____

Describing/Plot

Plot is what happens at the beginning, middle, and end of a story. Action words **describe** the plot.

Directions Use action words to describe what happens at the beginning, middle, and end of a story you know.

Beginning: _____

Middle: _____

End: _____

_____

_____

Adverbs

An **adverb** tells more about an action word. It often tells *when* or *where*.

Directions Circle the adverbs that tell *when*.

1. He started at a new school yesterday.

2. He got there early.

Think, Talk, and Write

Directions Reread **New Changes** and **A New School** on Student Worktext pages 136–137.

3. Talk with a partner about difficult changes. Read your Weekly Concept Journal on page 148. Change or add to what you wrote.

Name _____

Weather Changes

Directions Write the letter of the phrase that gives the meaning of each word.

1. _____ branches   **A.** a time when you take food and eat it outdoors

2. _____ picnic   **B.** in a short time from now

3. _____ outside   **C.** outdoors in nature

4. _____ soon   **D.** parts of a tree that grow out from it

5. _____ weather   **E.** the temperature and the wind, rain, or sun

---

The Sound /ü/ Spelled *ew, ue, ui, oo*

The *oo* in *moon* sounds like the *ue* in *glue*.

Directions Circle the words with the same vowel sound as *moon* and *glue*.

soon   foot   few   cook   stew   tool   suit   build

Name _____

Evaluating/Details and Facts

Facts are pieces of information that are true. **Details** can tell more about facts. We use the words *each* and *every* for **evaluating** how things are the same.

Directions Finish the sentences. Use the words **each** or **every**.

1. _____ snowflake is different.

2. The weather changes _____ day.

Adverbs

An **adverb** often tells *how* someone does something.

Directions Circle the adverbs that tell *how*.

3. The old man walked slowly.

4. The children played happily.

Think, Talk, and Write

Directions Reread **Weather Changes** and **Stormy Weather** on Student Worktext pages 142–143.

5. Talk about weather changes with a partner. Read your Weekly Concept Journal on page 154. Change or add to what you wrote.

Doing a Good Job

Vocabulary

ambulance	operator	responsible
fire truck	quickly	

Directions Finish the sentences. Use the words in the box.

1. People must act _____ in an emergency.

2. An _____ answers 9-1-1 calls.

3. Sometimes people are hurt and need an _____ .

4. Sometimes a _____ must rush to a place.

5. These people are _____ for saving lives.

Directions Use two vocabulary words in sentences of your own. Use these sentence starters if you need help.

People call 9-1-1 when...   In an emergency...

6. _____

_____

7. _____

_____

Name _____

Adding Suffixes

Directions Circle the suffix in each word.

1. teacher

2. actor

3. nicely

4. selfish

5. careful

6. quickly

7. feverish

8. operator

9. joyful

10. singer

Directions Add a suffix to each word to complete the sentence.

11. (paint) The _____ stood on a ladder as he worked.

12. (green) The stone has a _____ tint.

13. (peace) The boys felt _____ looking at the stars in the night sky.

14. (slow) The clouds moved _____ across the sky.

Describing

Directions Circle the words that tell about actions.

1. The operator spoke calmly.

2. The siren blared loudly.

3. The fire trucks arrived quickly.

4. The people inside got out safely.

5. The fire was put out completely.

Main Idea and Details

Directions Read the paragraph. Complete the sentences that tell the main idea and one detail.

Firefighters are brave. They rush inside burning buildings to help people. They know first aid, too.

Main Idea: Firefighters _____

_____ .

Detail: Firefighters _____

_____ .

Name _____

Pronouns

Directions Read the sentences. Circle the pronouns.

1. She is a 9-1-1 operator.

2. He drives a fire truck.

3. You must act quickly in an emergency.

4. I am a responsible person.

5. They are working together to save lives.

6. We saw the ambulance.

Directions Finish each sentence. Choose a pronoun that goes with the verb.

7. _____ want to be a firefighter.

8. _____ is an operator.

9. _____ are responsible.

10. _____ called 9-1-1.

Name _____

Produce Language

My Weekly Concept Journal

Directions Write your answers in the space provided.

Day 1 _____

_____

_____

_____

Day 2 _____

_____

_____

_____

_____

Day 3 _____

_____

_____

_____

Day 4 _____

_____

_____

_____

_____

Name _____

Produce Language

My Weekly Concept Journal

Directions Write 2 or 3 sentences to answer the weekly question.

Why should we be responsible for doing a good job?

_____

_____

_____

_____

_____

_____

_____

_____

_____

_____

_____

_____

_____

_____

_____

_____

_____

_____

_____

_____

Name _____

Helping Our Community

Vocabulary

bags	**members**	**unpack**
boxes	**repack**	

Directions Finish the sentences. Use the words in the box.

1. Community _____ have a food drive.

2. Some people bring _____ of food.

3. Others _____ the food.

4. Then they _____ the food.

5. They give _____ of food
to people who need it.

_____

Directions Use two vocabulary words in sentences of your
own. Use these sentence starters if you need help.
A food drive...   Workers...

6. _____

    _____

7. _____

    _____

Name _____

Adding Prefixes

Directions Circle the prefix in each word.

1. repack

2. unpack

3. disagree

4. rewrite

5. oversee

6. redo

7. undo

8. prefix

9. overlook

10. dishonest

Directions Add a prefix to each word to finish the sentences.

11. (appear) She watched the moon _____ behind the clouds.

12. (heat) _____ the oven before you put in the cake.

13. (tie) Luis stopped running to _____ his shoelaces.

14. (lock) Anna used her key to _____ the door.

15. (due) The library books were _____ .

Sequencing

Directions These pictures are not in order. Label what happens **first, next,** and **last.** Then write a sentence about each.

_____   _____   _____

First: _____

Next: _____

Last: _____

_____

Steps in a Process

Directions What do you do first, next, and last? Draw pictures that show each step in making a sand castle. Write a sentence about each step.

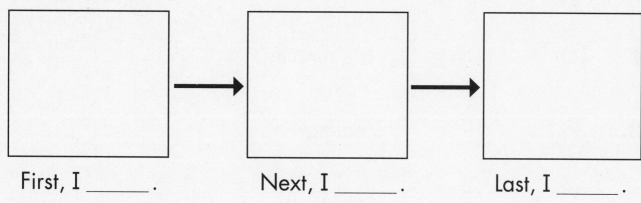

Name _____

Singular and Plural Pronouns

Directions Read the sentences. Each has a pronoun. Write whether the pronoun is **singular** or **plural.**

1. They unpack the food.   _____

2. She puts the food into bags.   _____

3. We give the food away.   _____

4. He takes a box of food.   _____

5. I like helping with the food drive.   _____

Directions Complete each sentence with a pronoun that goes with the picture.

6. _____ is little.

7. _____ are running.

8. _____ is eating.

9. _____ is skipping.

Produce Language

My Weekly Concept Journal

Directions Write your answers in the space provided.

Day 1 _____

_____

_____

_____

_____

Day 2 _____

_____

_____

_____

_____

Day 3 _____

_____

_____

_____

_____

Day 4 _____

_____

_____

_____

_____

Name _____

Produce Language

My Weekly Concept Journal

Directions Write 2 or 3 sentences to answer the weekly question.

How can we be responsible community members?

_____
_____
_____
_____
_____
_____
_____
_____
_____
_____
_____
_____
_____
_____
_____
_____
_____
_____
_____

Taking Care of Pets

Vocabulary

cage	forgot	owners
parrot	knows	safe

Directions Finish each sentence. Use the words in the box.

1. She has a pet _____.

2. It lives in a _____ .

3. This keeps the bird _____.

4. She _____ that cats can kill birds.

5. Once, she _____ to change the water.

6. Pet _____ should be responsible.

Directions Use two vocabulary words in sentences of your own. Use these sentence starters if you need help.

A pet bird...   People...

7. _____

8. _____

Name _____

Silent Consonants *kn, wr, gn,* and *mb*

Directions Circle the silent consonant in each word.

1.   lamb

2. **STOP**   sign

3.   wrist

4.   knee

Directions Circle the correct word to complete each sentence.

5. I no/know the capital of California.

6. Cats can climb/clime trees.

7. I ring/wring out my wet bathing suit before I put it in my bag.

8. A mouse can nor/gnaw through a box.

Retelling

Directions Circle the action verbs that tell about the past.

1. The parrot stayed in its cage.

2. He ran to the pet store.

3. I cleaned the cage.

4. She changed the water in the cage.

5. The pet grew bigger.

Plot and Theme

Directions Read the story. One sentence tells the theme. The other sentences tell the plot. Write each sentence on the correct line.

   Luis found a nest that fell from a tree. He got help for the baby bird inside. Luis set the bird free. Luis loves animals.

Theme: _____

Plot

Beginning: _____

Middle: _____

End: _____

Name _____

Using *I* and *Me*

Directions Read the sentences. Circle *I* and *me*.

1. I like animals.

2. Animals like me.

3. I throw a ball to my dog.

4. My dog brings the ball back to me.

Directions Finish the sentences. Use **I** and **me.**

5. _____ have a pet parrot.

6. My parents gave the parrot to _____.

7. _____ feed my pet.

8. _____ think the parrot likes _____.

Produce Language

My Weekly Concept Journal

Directions Write your answers in the space provided.

Day 1 _____
_____
_____
_____
_____

Day 2 _____
_____
_____
_____
_____

Day 3 _____
_____
_____
_____
_____

Day 4 _____
_____
_____
_____
_____

Name _____

Produce Language

My Weekly Concept Journal

Directions Write 2 or 3 sentences to answer the weekly question.

How can we be responsible animal owners?

_____

_____

_____

_____

_____

_____

_____

_____

_____

_____

_____

_____

_____

_____

_____

_____

_____

_____

Friends and Neighbors

Vocabulary

streets	laugh
trash	neighborhood

Directions Finish the sentences. Use the words in the box.

1. She moved to a new _____ .

2. People did not throw _____ on the ground.

3. The _____ were clean.

4. She likes to _____ and have fun with friends.

Directions Use three vocabulary words in sentences of your own. Use these sentence starters if you need help.

Friends...   We live...   Good neighbors pick up...

5. _____

_____

6. _____

_____

7. _____

_____

Name _____

/f/ Spelled *ph* and *gh*

Directions Circle the word that is spelled correctly.

1.   laugh   laff

2.   fone   phone

3.   rough   ruf

4.   foto   photo

Directions Finish the sentences. Use the words in the box.

graph	enough	tough	cough

5. I cover my mouth when I _____.

6. The meat is too _____ to cut.

7. There is _____ snow to go sledding.

8. We made a bar _____ in math class.

Explaining

Directions Complete each sentence. Tell why you like someone, some place, or something.

1. I like _____ because _____ .

2. I like _____ because _____ .

3. I like _____ because _____ .

Author's Purpose

Directions Circle the author's purpose for writing.

4. The author writes about responsible people because
she wants people to be more responsible.

5. The author writes a letter because
he wants to share news with a friend.

6. The author writes a story because
she wants children to have fun reading.

7. The author writes a cookbook because
she wants to help people make better meals.

Name _____

Different Kinds of Pronouns

Directions Read the sentences. Circle the pronouns before the action words. Underline the pronouns after the action words.

1. We helped Marsha clean up.

2. Carlos walked next to him.

3. They took the children to the park.

4. I invited Ana to the party.

5. You called me on the phone.

_____

Directions Circle the pronoun that finishes the sentence.

6. We/Us cleaned up the neighborhood.

7. She helped they/them take away trash.

8. He/Him is my best friend.

9. They/Them are good neighbors.

10. Mom drove she/her home.

Produce Language

My Weekly Concept Journal

Directions Write your answers in the space provided.

Day 1 _____
_____
_____
_____
_____

Day 2 _____
_____
_____
_____
_____

Day 3 _____
_____
_____
_____
_____

Day 4 _____
_____
_____
_____
_____

Name _____

Produce Language

My Weekly Concept Journal

Directions Write 2 or 3 sentences to answer the weekly question.

How can we be responsible friends and neighbors?

_____

_____

_____

_____

_____

_____

_____

_____

_____

_____

_____

_____

_____

_____

_____

_____

_____

_____

_____

Fixing Mistakes

Vocabulary

talked	baseball	mistake
window	broke	truth

Directions Finish the sentences. Use words from the box.

1. Everyone makes a _____ sometime.

2. Maybe you _____ something by accident.

3. Sometimes it is hard to tell the _____.

4. A boy was playing _____.

5. The ball went through a _____.

6. He _____ about it.

_____

Directions Use two vocabulary words in sentences of your own. Use these sentence starters if you need help.

Responsible people...   The boy...

7. _____

_____

8. _____

_____

Name _____

/ȯ/ Spelled *aw*, *au*, *au(gh)*, and *al*

Directions Write the word that names the picture.

1. 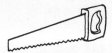 s____

2.  ____to

3. b____l

4. ch____k

Directions Finish the sentences. Use the words in the box.

author	caught	hawk	talk

5. The police _____ the robber.

6. My class wrote letters to a famous _____.

7. I like to _____ to my friends.

8. I see a _____ in that tree.

Literary Analysis

Directions Write about things you want to do.

1. I want to _____ .

2. I want to _____ .

3. I want to _____ .

Author's Purpose

Directions Finish each sentence. Tell why you think an author writes something.

4. An author writes a joke book to

_____

_____ .

5. An author writes a story about good neighbors to

_____

_____ .

6. An author writes a math book to

_____

_____ .

Name _____

Contractions

Directions Circle the contractions in the sentences.

1. He didn't want to break the window.

2. The neighbor wasn't angry.

3. He doesn't want to lie.

4. He isn't in trouble.

5. Some mistakes aren't so bad.

6. The neighbor hasn't fixed the window yet.

Directions Circle the contraction that matches the underlined words.

7. He <u>does not</u> want to play. (isn't, doesn't)

8. She <u>cannot</u> find the ball. (won't, can't)

9. It <u>is not</u> time for lunch. (isn't, hasn't)

10. They <u>are not</u> ready to go. (aren't, wasn't)

Name _____

Produce Language

My Weekly Concept Journal

Directions Write your answers in the space provided.

Day 1 _____

_____

_____

_____

Day 2 _____

_____

_____

_____

Day 3 _____

_____

_____

_____

Day 4 _____

_____

_____

_____

_____

Name _____

Produce Language

My Weekly Concept Journal

Directions Write 2 or 3 sentences to answer the weekly question.

How can we be responsible when we make a mistake?

_____

_____

_____

_____

_____

_____

_____

_____

_____

_____

_____

_____

_____

_____

_____

_____

_____

_____

Doing a Good Job

Directions Write the letter of the phrase that gives the meaning of each word.

1. _____ fire truck

A. someone who controls the telephone calls made to or from a place

2. _____ operator

B. done or happening in a short time

3. _____ quickly

C. a large vehicle with hoses and water that helps firefighters stop fires

4. _____ responsible

D. take care of someone or something

Adding Suffixes

Suffixes are added to the end of words. They change the meanings of words.

Directions Add the suffix. Write the new word. Then use the new word in a sentence.

5. act + or _____

Sentence: _____

6. patient + ly _____

Sentence: _____

Name _____

Describing/Main Idea and Details

A **main idea** is the most important idea in a story. **Details** tell about the main idea. Words that end in *-ly* **describe** actions.

Directions Circle the words that tell about actions.

1. They put out the fire quickly.

2. The firefighters acted bravely.

3. The ambulance arrived immediately.

Pronouns

Pronouns replace nouns in sentences.

Directions Circle the pronouns in the sentences.

4. He was surprised at the party.

5. I want to buy a red bike.

6. Did you read that book?

Think, Talk, and Write

Directions Reread **Doing a Good Job** and **Calling 9–1–1** on Student Worktext pages 150–151.

7. Talk about responsibility with a partner. Read your Weekly Concept Journal on page 170. Change or add to what you wrote.

Helping Our Community

Directions Write the letter of the phrase that gives the meaning of each word.

1. _____ bags

A. to pack again

2. _____ boxes

B. to take things out of a box or bag

3. _____ members

C. containers with four straight sides, usually made of paper or wood

4. _____ repack

D. containers made of cloth, paper, plastic, or leather, used for carrying

5. _____ unpack

E. people who have joined a group or organization

Adding Prefixes

Prefixes are added to the beginning of words. They change the meanings of words.

Directions Add the prefix. Write the new word. Circle the correct definition of the new word.

6. un + able _____   not able   able again

7. dis + continue _____   start again   stop

Name _____

Sequencing/Steps in a Process

We use words such as *first*, *next*, and *last* to tell the **sequence** of **steps in a process.**

Directions Write the steps for washing your hair.

1. First, _____ .

2. Next, _____ .

3. Last, _____ .

Singular and Plural Pronouns

Singular pronouns stand for one person, place, or thing.
Plural pronouns stand for more than one person, place, or thing.

Directions Circle the singular pronouns. Draw a line under the plural pronouns.

4. We have a new baby brother.

5. She is a good friend of mine.

Think, Talk, and Write

Directions Reread **Helping Our Community** and **Food Drive** on Student Worktext pages 156–157.

6. Talk about responsibility and community with a partner. Read your Weekly Concept Journal on page 176. Change or add to what you wrote.

Taking Care of Pets

Directions Write the letter of the phrase that gives the meaning of each word.

1. ____ cage

2. ____ parrot

3. ____ forgot

4. ____ knows

5. ____ owners

6. ____ safe

A. a box made of metal wires, in which you keep birds or animals

B. not in danger of being harmed

C. has information about something

D. a brightly-colored tropical bird with a curved beak

E. was unable to think of or remember

F. people who have something that belongs to them

Silent Consonants *kn, wr, gn,* and *mb*

Some words include consonant pairs with a silent consonant, such as the *k* in *know*.

Directions Circle the words in each sentence that have a silent consonant.

7. My grandmother knit me a sweater.

8. I wrote a letter to my pen pal.

9. A bird will take a crumb of bread.

10. A gnat is a tiny insect.

Name _____

Retelling/Plot and Theme

Theme is the main idea of a story. **Plot** is what happens. We use past tense action verbs to **retell** a story.

Directions Think of a story you read in a book. Write three sentences that retell the plot. Use an action verb in each sentence.

1. Beginning: _____

2. Middle: _____

3. End: _____

Using *I* and *Me*

I and *me* are pronouns we use to describe ourselves.

Directions Finish the sentences. Use **I** or **me.**

4. ____ walk my dog, Skip.

5. Skip shows he likes ____ by licking my face.

Think, Talk, and Write

Directions Reread **Taking Care of Pets** and **Brett's Parrot** on Student Worktext pages 162–163.

6. Talk about being a responsible pet owner with a partner. Read your Weekly Concept Journal on page 182. Change or add to what you wrote.

Friends and Neighbors

Directions Write the letter of the phrase that gives the meaning of each word.

1. _____ streets

A. to make a sound that shows that you are happy

2. _____ trash

B. a small area of a town and the people who live there

3. _____ laugh

C. roads in a town or city

4. _____ neighborhood

D. waste material such as old food and dirty paper

/f/ Spelled *ph* and *gh*

Some words have a consonant pair that sounds like /f/ but is spelled *gh* or *ph*.

Directions Circle the word in each sentence with the consonant pair *gh* or *ph* that sounds like /f/.

5. We put my class photo on the refrigerator.

6. Sandpaper feels rough.

7. Learning phonics helps us spell words.

Name _____

Explaining/Author's Purpose

The **author's purpose** tells why an author writes something. The word *because* helps us **explain,** or tell *why*.

Directions Finish the sentence.

1. If I were an author I would tell about _____

because _____ .

Different Kinds of Pronouns

Some **pronouns** come before action words. Other pronouns come after action words.

Directions Finish the sentences. Use a pronoun.

2. _____ like my neighbors.

3. I decided to call _____ .

Think, Talk, and Write

Directions Reread **Friends and Neighbors** and **Helping Out** on Student Worktext pages 168–169.

4. Talk with a partner about how we can be responsible friends and neighbors. Read your Weekly Concept Journal on page 188. Change or add to what you wrote.

Fixing Mistakes

Directions Write the letter of the phrase that gives the meaning of each word.

1. _____ talked

A. the correct, or true, facts

2. _____ window

B. came apart or was hurt

3. _____ baseball

C. said things to someone; spoke

4. _____ broke

D. a game that is played on a special field with a ball and a long stick

5. _____ mistake

E. something that is not correct

6. _____ truth

F. an opening with glass across it in a wall of a building

/ȯ/ Spelled *aw*, *au*, *augh*, *a*, and *al*

The vowel sound /ȯ/ can be spelled *aw* as in *saw*, *au* as in *auto*, *augh* as in *caught*, *a* as in *ball*, and *al* as in *talk*.

Directions Circle the words with the /ȯ/ *sound*.

yawn	well	fall
cause	crawl	full
coat	cream	draw

Name _____

Literary Analysis/Author's Purpose

The **author's purpose** tells why an author writes something.

Directions Reread **The Mistake** on page 175 of your Student Worktext. What is the author's purpose for writing this story?

1. The author wrote the story to _____.

_____

Contractions

A **contraction** is a short way to say or write two words.

Directions Write the contractions.

2. are + not _____

4. do + not _____

3. is + not _____

5. has + not _____

Think, Talk, and Write

Directions Reread **Fixing Mistakes** and **The Mistake** on Student Worktext pages 174–175.

6. Talk with a partner about taking responsibility for a mistake. Read your Weekly Concept Journal on page 194. Change or add to what you wrote.

Name _____

Sports

Vocabulary

bat	wood	didn't
players	cheers	watched

Directions Finish the sentences. Use the words from the box.

1. People _____ a baseball game.

2. A man swung the _____.

3. The _____ cracked when it hit the ball.

4. The _____ stopped and looked.

5. They _____ think it would break.

6. Everyone _____ when the home team scores.

Directions Use two vocabulary words in sentences of your own. Use these sentence starters if you need help.
They went to the game...   The family...

7. _____

_____

8. _____

_____

Name _____

Using Contractions

Directions Write the contractions.

1. we + are _____

2. I + have _____

3. It + had _____

4. will + not _____

Directions Finish the sentences. Use the contractions you wrote above.

5. _____ been raining all day.

6. _____ going on a trip.

7. _____ a flat tire on my bike.

8. He _____ play goalie.

Comparing

Directions Finish each sentence. Use **both** and **like.**

1. Joe is tall. Sam is tall.

Joe and Sam are _____ tall.

Joe, _____ Sam, is tall.

2. The skirt has dots on it. The shirt has dots on it.

The shirt and the skirt _____ have dots.

The shirt, _____ the skirt, has dots.

Compare and Contrast

Directions Finish the sentences. Tell how two things are alike and different. **like   both   different from**

3. A basketball is _____ a baseball.

They are _____ round.

A basketball is _____ a baseball.

It is bigger.

4. A bee can fly. A bird can fly.

A bee is _____ a bird. They

_____ can fly.

A bee is _____ a bird. It is an insect.

Name _____

Capital Letters

Directions Write the names of three days of the week. Use a capital letter at the beginning of each word.

1. _____

2. _____

3. _____

Directions Write the names of three months of the year. Use a capital letter at the beginning of each word.

4. _____

5. _____

6. _____

Directions Circle the words and titles that should begin with a capital letter.

7. We invited mr. and mrs. smith to come for thanksgiving.

8. Mom is taking me to dr. jones on tuesday.

9. They go on vacation every july.

Produce Language

My Weekly Concept Journal

Directions Write your answers in the space provided.

Day 1 _____

_____

_____

_____

Day 2 _____

_____

_____

_____

_____

Day 3 _____

_____

_____

_____

_____

Day 4 _____

_____

_____

_____

_____

Name _____

Produce Language

My Weekly Concept Journal

Directions Write 2 or 3 sentences to answer the weekly question.

Why are sports traditions important in our country?

_____

_____

_____

_____

_____

_____

_____

_____

_____

_____

_____

_____

_____

_____

_____

_____

_____

_____

Flag Celebrations

Vocabulary

flag	**stars**	**stripes**
celebration	**freedom**	**tradition**

Directions Finish the sentences. Use the words in the box.

1. The American _____ is red, white, and blue.

2. It has white _____ on a blue background.

3. It has red and white _____ .

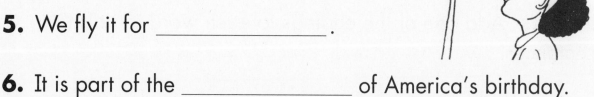

4. It stands for _____ .

5. We fly it for _____ .

6. It is part of the _____ of America's birthday.

Directions Use two vocabulary words in sentences of your own. Use these sentence starters if you need help.
America...   A holiday is a...

7. _____

_____

8. _____

_____

Name _____

Base Words and Endings

Directions Add the ending to the base word to make a new word.

1.   talk + ed _____

2.    paint + ing _____

3.   bake + s _____

4.   box + es _____

Directions Add one of the endings to each word to finish the sentences.

5. (tool) He used _____ to fix the roof.

6. (rain) It was _____ all day.

7. (cook) She _____ dinner last night.

8. (glass) I washed two _____ in the sink.

Defining

Directions Complete the sentences with names of holidays.

1. _____ is a holiday.

2. _____ is a holiday.

3. _____ is a holiday.

4. _____ is a holiday.

Classify and Categorize

Directions Look at the pictures. Name the group.

5.  They are all _____.

6. They are all _____.

7. They are all _____.

Name _____

Quotation Marks

Directions Circle the quotation marks in the sentences below.

1. "Happy Fourth of July!" I said.

2. My mother said, "Let's go to the celebration."

3. "This is a tradition," said Grandma.

4. Luis said, "I like this holiday."

Directions Put quotation marks where they belong in the sentences below.

5. I asked, Where are my shoes?

6. Your shoes are in the car, said Mom.

7. Please close the door, said Dad.

8. She said, I'm ready to go.

Name _____

Produce Language

My Weekly Concept Journal

Directions Write your answers in the space provided.

Day 1 _____

_____

_____

_____

Day 2 _____

_____

_____

_____

_____

Day 3 _____

_____

_____

_____

_____

Day 4 _____

_____

_____

_____

Name _____

Produce Language

My Weekly Concept Journal

Directions Write 2 or 3 sentences to answer the weekly question.

What traditions and celebrations involve our country's flag?

_____

_____

_____

_____

_____

_____

_____

_____

_____

_____

_____

_____

_____

_____

_____

_____

_____

_____

Family Celebrations

Vocabulary

| basket | candles | favorite | happiness |

Directions Finish the sentences. Use the words in the box.

1. Family celebrations bring _____ to many.

2. What is your _____ holiday meal?

3. A _____ of fruit is a nice gift.

4. The family lights _____ on special days.

Directions Use three vocabulary words in sentences of your own. Use these sentence starters if you need help.
Families celebrate...   Friends give...
Holidays bring...

5. _____

_____

6. _____

_____

7. _____

_____

Name _____

Common Syllables

Directions Circle the last syllable of each word.

1. picture

2. nature

3.  celebration

4. $9 - 3 = 6$ subtraction

_____

Directions Finish the sentences. Use the words above.

5. I like going to the woods and seeing everything

   in _____ .

6. I have ten _____ problems for homework.

7. I am excited about the birthday _____ .

8. I drew a _____ of my family.

Draw Conclusions

Directions Complete the sentences with a conclusion about each picture.

1. I think that _____

_____ .

2. I think that _____

_____ .

Draw Conclusions

Directions Use the picture and what you know to draw a conclusion about the Fourth of July.

3. I think that the Fourth of July is

_____

_____ .

Name _____

Using Commas

Directions Circle the commas in this letter.

January 4, 2010

Dear Grandma,

Happy New Year!
I miss you.

Love,
Molly

Mrs. Sara Feld
222 Oak Hill Lane
Walpole,
New Hampshire 03608

Directions The dates and places in the sentences below are **not** written correctly. Add commas where they belong.

1. I have a pen pal in Paris France.

2. My grandmother was born in San Diego California,

on October 29 1956.

3. That movie was made in London England.

Produce Language

My Weekly Concept Journal

Directions Write your answers in the space provided.

Day 1 _____

_____

_____

_____

Day 2 _____

_____

_____

_____

_____

Day 3 _____

_____

_____

_____

_____

Day 4 _____

_____

_____

_____

_____

Name _____

Produce Language

My Weekly Concept Journal

Directions Write 2 or 3 sentences to answer the weekly question.

Why are family celebrations special?

_____

_____

_____

_____

_____

_____

_____

_____

_____

_____

_____

_____

_____

_____

_____

_____

_____

_____

_____

Cowboy Life

Vocabulary

cattle	herd	traveled
cowboy	tireless	

Directions Finish the sentences. Use the words in the box.

1. Carlos read a story about a _____ named Bob.

2. Bob _____ to a new town.

3. He helped move a _____ of cows.

4. Someone tried to steal the _____ .

5. Bob was _____ and never went to sleep.

Directions Use two vocabulary words in sentences of your own. Use these sentence starters if you need help.

Long ago, out West,...   **Men on horses...**

6. _____

_____

7. _____

_____

Name _____

Suffixes

Directions Circle the suffix in each word.

1. tireless   **4.** usable

2. lovable   **5.** hopeless

3. sadness   **6.** terrible

Directions Finish the sentences. Use the words in the box.

| **happiness** | **responsible** | **agreeable** | **helpless** |

7. Some baby animals are _____.

8. You have to be _____ if you want to take care of a pet.

9. Simple things can bring _____.

10. We like our neighbor because he is so _____.

Cause-and-Effect Relationship

Directions Circle the cause-and-effect word in each sentence.

1. He stayed home from school because he was sick.

2. She went to bed early because she was tired.

3. The ice cubes melted because I left them on the table.

4. He took an umbrella because it was raining.

Cause and Effect

Directions Write the cause and effect for each sentence.

We took the bus because it was too far to walk.

5. Effect: _____

6. Cause: _____

We played inside because it was raining.

7. Effect: _____

8. Cause: _____

Name _____

Compound Sentences

Directions Circle the connecting word in each compound sentence.

1. He wanted to be a cowboy, but he didn't know how to ride a horse.

2. I like to read about cowboys, so I got some books from the library.

3. Cowboys ride horses, and they herd cattle.

4. Let's go see a cowboy movie, or let's pretend to be cowboys.

Directions Use connecting words to connect the sentences below. Don't forget the comma.

The cowboy wore a hat. The cowboy wore boots.

5. _____

The cattle needed food. There was no grass.

6. _____

The herd was big. There was only one cowboy.

7. _____

Produce Language

My Weekly Concept Journal

Directions Write your answers in the space provided.

Day 1 _____

_____

_____

_____

_____

Day 2 _____

_____

_____

_____

_____

Day 3 _____

_____

_____

_____

_____

Day 4 _____

_____

_____

_____

_____

Name _____

Produce Language

My Weekly Concept Journal

Directions Write 2 or 3 sentences to answer the weekly question.

What can we learn about cowboy traditions?

_____

_____

_____

_____

_____

_____

_____

_____

_____

_____

_____

_____

_____

_____

_____

_____

_____

_____

_____

Name _____

Sharing Celebrations

Vocabulary

dumplings	meal	guests
festival	dragon	midway

Directions Finish the sentences. Use the words in the box.

1. A _____ is held in China.

2. Boats are painted to look like a _____ .

3. People invite _____ to eat with them.

4. They share a wonderful _____ .

5. One food they serve is _____ .

6. They got a phone call _____ through dinner.

Directions Use two vocabulary words in sentences of your own. Use these sentence starters if you need help.
They celebrate...   In China...

7. _____

_____

8. _____

_____

Prefixes

Directions Circle the prefix in each word.

1. midway

2. nonstop

3. midsummer

4. nonfiction

5. midnight

6. nonsense

7. mistreat

8. misspell

Directions Add a prefix to each word. Use the new word to finish the sentence.

9. (fat) She drinks _____ milk.

10. (place) Don't _____ that letter!

11. (day) Many people eat a _____ meal.

Draw Conclusions

Directions Use special words to tell how you feel about the following.

1. I think that the Chinese Dragon Boat Festival is _____ because _____ .

2. I think our teacher is _____ because _____ .

3. I think spending time with my family is _____ because _____ .

Draw Conclusions

Directions Complete the sentences that draw conclusions about each picture.

4. I think they won the game

because _____ .

5. I think it is a windy day

because _____ .

Name _____

Paragraphs

Directions Finish these sentences about paragraphs.

1. A paragraph is a group of _____ .

2. When you indent, you are adding _____ .

_____

Directions Write a paragraph about a celebration you enjoy.

_____

_____

_____

_____

_____

_____

_____

_____

_____

_____

Produce Language

My Weekly Concept Journal

Directions Write your answers in the space provided.

Day 1 _____
_____
_____
_____

Day 2 _____
_____
_____
_____
_____

Day 3 _____
_____
_____
_____
_____

Day 4 _____
_____
_____
_____

Name _____

Produce Language

My Weekly Concept Journal

Directions Write 2 or 3 sentences to answer the weekly question.

How are traditions and celebrations shared?

_____

_____

_____

_____

_____

_____

_____

_____

_____

_____

_____

_____

_____

_____

_____

_____

_____

_____

Sports

Directions Write the letter of the phrase that gives the meaning of each word.

1. _____ bat

A. the material of which the trunks and branches of trees are made

2. _____ players

B. a long piece of wood used for hitting the ball in baseball

3. _____ wood

C. shouts of happiness or support

4. _____ cheers

D. people who play a game or a sport

5. _____ didn't

E. looked at something and paid attention to it

6. _____ watched

F. did not

Using Contractions

A **contraction** is a short way to say or write two words.

Directions Write the contraction.

7. do not _____

9. will not _____

8. we are _____

10. I have _____

Name _____

Comparing/Compare and Contrast

When you **compare,** you tell how things are alike. When you **contrast,** you tell how things are different.

Directions Finish the sentences to compare and contrast.

1. A ball is _____ a marble. They are _____ round.

A ball is _____ a marble. It is bigger.

Capital Letters

The names of days, months, and holidays begin with a **capital letter.** So do people's names and titles, such as *Dr. Smith.*

Directions Write about your week. Use capital letters correctly.

2. _____

_____

Think, Talk, and Write

Directions Reread **Sports** and **A New Bat** on Student Worktext pages 182–183.

3. Talk with a partner about sports traditions. Read your Weekly Concept Journal on page 210. Change or add to what you wrote.

Flag Celebrations

Directions Write the letter of the phrase that gives the meaning of each word.

1. _____ flag

A. the state of being able to do what you want

2. _____ stars

B. long thin lines of color

3. _____ stripes

C. a piece of cloth with a special pattern on it, used as the symbol of a country

4. _____ celebration

D. a belief or custom that has existed for a long time

5. _____ freedom

E. shapes with five or six points

6. _____ tradition

F. a party that you have because something good has happened

Base Words and Endings

Word endings change how the word is used.

Directions Underline the base words. Circle the endings.

7. walking

9. foxes

8. smallest

10. stayed

Name _____

Defining/Classify and Categorize

We can put like things into groups.

Directions Look at the picture. Name the group. Finish the sentences.

1. Group: _____

2. _____ are fruit.

3. _____ are fruit.

Quotation Marks

Quotation marks go at the beginning and end of what someone says.

Directions Put quotation marks where they belong in the sentences below.

4. I don't want to miss the celebration, said Pablo.

5. Eric said, I have the flags.

6. Let's go, said Anna.

Think, Talk, and Write

Directions Reread **Flag Celebrations** and **Our Flag** on Student Worktext pages 188–189.

7. Talk with a partner about holiday traditions. Read your Weekly Concept Journal on page 216. Change or add to what you wrote.

Family Celebrations

Directions Write the letter of the phrase that gives the meaning of each word.

1. _____ basket

A. someone or something that you like more than any others

2. _____ candles

B. the state of being pleased

3. _____ favorite

C. a container made of thin pieces of wood or dried plants used for carrying things

4. _____ happiness

D. pieces of wax with strings in the middle that you burn to give light

Common Syllables

Recognizing common syllables can help you read unfamiliar words.

Directions Put the word parts together to make a new word. Then, write a sentence with the new word.

5. educa + tion _____

Sentence: _____

6. pic + ture _____

Sentence: _____

Name _____

Draw Conclusions/Draw Conclusions

We use what we read and what we know to **draw conclusions.**

Directions Finish the sentences with a conclusion about each picture.

1. I think that _____ .

2. I think that _____ .

Using Commas

We use **commas** to write dates and addresses.

Directions Write the dates. Use commas.

3. The date today is: _____

4. My birth date is: _____

Think, Talk, and Write

Directions Reread **Family Celebrations** and **Celebrate Diwali!** on Student Worktext pages 194–195.

5. Talk with a partner about family celebrations. Read your Weekly Concept Journal on page 222. Change or add to what you wrote.

Name _____

Cowboy Life

Directions Write the letter of the phrase that gives the meaning of each word.

1. _____ cattle   **A.** a group of animals of the same kind

2. _____ cowboy   **B.** a man who rides a horse and takes care of cattle

3. _____ herd   **C.** made a trip from one place to another

4. _____ tireless   **D.** large animals kept for their meat, milk, and skins

5. _____ traveled   **E.** not ever getting tired; always having energy

Suffixes

Suffixes are added to the ends of words. They change the meanings of words.

Direction Add the suffix. Write the new word. Circle the correct definition of the new word.

6. bend + able _____ able to bend   without bending

7. fear + less _____ very afraid   not afraid

8. dark + ness _____ not dark   in the dark

Name _____

Cause-and-Effect Relationship/Cause and Effect

An **effect** is something that happens. The **cause** is why it happens.

Directions Underline the cause and circle the effect.

1. I slept too late because the alarm did not go off.

2. She could not unlock the door because she forgot her key.

Compound Sentences

A **compound sentence** contains two sentences that are joined by a comma and a connecting word, such as: *and, or, but, yet,* and *so.*

Directions Combine the sentences to make a compound sentence. Use the connecting word *and.*

3. She liked music. She was learning to play the recorder.

_____

4. It was raining. She saw a rainbow.

_____

Think, Talk, and Write

Directions Reread **Cowboy Life** and **Today's Cowboys** on Student Worktext pages 200–201.

5. Talk with a partner about cowboys and the Old West. Read your Weekly Concept Journal on page 228. Change or add to what you wrote.

Sharing Celebrations

Directions Write the letter of the phrase that gives the meaning of each word.

1. _____ festival

A. the food that you eat at one time

2. _____ meal

B. a fierce animal in stories that has wings and can breathe out fire

3. _____ dragon

C. a set of special events

4. _____ guests

D. in the middle of

5. _____ midway

E. people who are visiting someone else's house

Prefixes

Prefixes are added to the beginning of words. They change the meanings of words.

Direction Add the prefix. Write the new word. Circle the correct definition of the new word.

6. mis + place _____

put in the middle of a place   put in the wrong place

7. mid + year _____

in the middle of the year   not every year

Name _____

Draw Conclusions/Draw Conclusions

We use what we read and what we know from real life to **draw conclusions.**

Directions Draw conclusions about the picture.
Finish the sentences.

1. I think that the girl is _____

because she is _____ .

Paragraphs

A **paragraph** is a group of sentences on a single topic.

Directions Write a paragraph about a person you know.

_____

_____

_____

_____

_____

_____

Think, Talk, and Write

Directions Reread **Sharing Celebrations** and **Dragon Boat Festival** on Student Worktext Worktext pages 206–207.

2. Talk with a partner about how traditions and celebrations are shared. Read your Weekly Concept Journal on page 234. Change or add to what you wrote.